MW00635377

Eclipse Bulletin:
Total Solar Eclipse
of
2024 April 08

Color Edition

Fred Espenak and **Jay Anderson**

Edition 1.0
August 2022

Eclipse Bulletin: Total Solar Eclipse of 2024 April 08 – Color Edition

Copyright © 2022 by Fred Espenak and Jay Anderson

All rights reserved. No part of this publication may be reproduced, distributed, or transmitted in any form or by any means, including photocopying, recording, or other electronic or mechanical methods, without the prior written permission of the publisher, except in the case of brief quotations embodied in critical reviews and certain other noncommercial uses permitted by copyright law. For permission requests, write to the publisher at the address below.

Astropixels Publishing

P.O. Box 16197

Portal, AZ 85632

www.astropixels.com/pubs

Printed in the United States of America

ISBN 978-1-941983-44-7

Astropixels Publication: AP043 (Version 1.0a)

First Edition

Front Cover: A global map illustrates the geographic regions within the path of the Moon's shadows during the total solar eclipse of 2024 April 08. A partial eclipse is visible from the large saddle-shaped zone outline with magenta and cyan curves. The narrow path of the total eclipse appears as the blue track. Map copyright © 2022 by Fred Espenak. More about the eclipse can be found at:

www.eclipsewise.com/news/2024.html

Back Cover Photo of Fred Espenak: Copyright © 2017 by Fred Espenak

Back Cover Photo of Jay Anderson: Copyright © 2015 by Fred Espenak

Table of Contents

The total solar eclipse of 2024 April 08 is the first to cross the continental USA since 2017. © 2015 Michael Zeiler

Section 1: Eclipse Predictions and Umbral Path

1.1 Introduction

On Monday, 2024 April 08, a total eclipse of the Sun will be visible from the contiguous United States for the first time since 2017. The track of the Moon's umbral shadow begins in the Pacific Ocean and crosses northern Mexico before reaching the USA. Traveling southwest to northeast, it sweeps through parts of fifteen states: Texas, Oklahoma, Arkansas, Missouri, Tennessee, Kentucky, Illinois, Indiana, Ohio, Michigan, Pennsylvania, New York, Vermont, New Hampshire, and Maine. The path of totality also crosses six Canadian provinces: Ontario, Quebec, New Brunswick, Prince Edward Island, Nova Scotia, and Newfoundland. Within the 101 to 124 mile-wide path of totality, the Moon will completely cover the Sun as the landscape is plunged into an eerie twilight and the Sun's glorious corona is revealed for nearly 4 ½ minutes. The Moon's penumbral shadow produces a partial eclipse visible from a much larger region covering most of North America.

The next total eclipse of the Sun visible coast to coast across the United States[1] does not occur until 2045 August 12. This rarity underscores the significance of the 2024 eclipse, which offers millions of Americans the opportunity to witness totality within 1,500 miles or less from home.

---

[1] A total eclipse on 2033 March 30 is visible from northwestern Alaska shortly after sunrise. Another total eclipse is visible from North Dakota, Montana, and Canada on 2044 August 23.

Figure 1–1: Orthographic Projection Map of 2024 Eclipse Path

Total Solar Eclipse of 2024 Apr 08

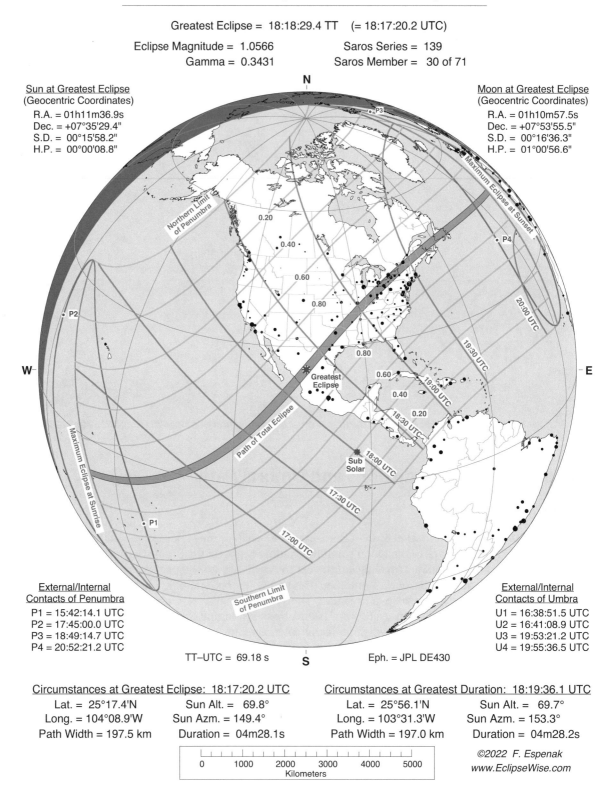

Greatest Eclipse = 18:18:29.4 TT   (= 18:17:20.2 UTC)

Eclipse Magnitude = 1.0566   Saros Series = 139
Gamma = 0.3431   Saros Member = 30 of 71

Sun at Greatest Eclipse
(Geocentric Coordinates)
R.A. = 01h11m36.9s
Dec. = +07°35'29.4"
S.D. = 00°15'58.2"
H.P. = 00°00'08.8"

Moon at Greatest Eclipse
(Geocentric Coordinates)
R.A. = 01h10m57.5s
Dec. = +07°53'55.5"
S.D. = 00°16'36.3"
H.P. = 01°00'56.6"

**External/Internal
Contacts of Penumbra**
P1 = 15:42:14.1 UTC
P2 = 17:45:00.0 UTC
P3 = 18:49:14.7 UTC
P4 = 20:52:21.2 UTC

**External/Internal
Contacts of Umbra**
U1 = 16:38:51.5 UTC
U2 = 16:41:08.9 UTC
U3 = 19:53:21.2 UTC
U4 = 19:55:36.5 UTC

TT–UTC = 69.18 s   Eph. = JPL DE430

Circumstances at Greatest Eclipse: 18:17:20.2 UTC
Lat. = 25°17.4'N   Sun Alt. = 69.8°
Long. = 104°08.9'W   Sun Azm. = 149.4°
Path Width = 197.5 km   Duration = 04m28.1s

Circumstances at Greatest Duration: 18:19:36.1 UTC
Lat. = 25°56.1'N   Sun Alt. = 69.7°
Long. = 103°31.3'W   Sun Azm. = 153.3°
Path Width = 197.0 km   Duration = 04m28.2s

©2022 F. Espenak
www.EclipseWise.com

Adapted from *21st Century Canon of Solar Eclipses,* Fred Espenak, 2016.

Photo 1–1: A sequence of images captures the partial phases and the solar corona visible only during totality. The total solar eclipse of 1999 August 11 from Lake Hazar, Turkey. © 1999 by F. Espenak, www.MrEclipse.com

1.2 Orthographic Projection Map of the Eclipse Path

When the Moon's penumbral shadow strikes Earth, a partial eclipse of the Sun is visible from that region. The Moon's apparent motion with respect to the Sun is relatively slow — the partial phases can last about three hours. During this time, the Moon's dark limb slowly creeps across the Sun's disk. Figure 1–1 is an orthographic projection map of Earth (adapted from Espenak 2016) showing the path of penumbral (partial) and umbral (total) eclipse. The daylight terminator is plotted for the instant of greatest eclipse[2] with north at the top. The map is centered over the point of greatest eclipse and is indicated with an asterisk symbol. The sub-solar point[3] at that instant is also shown.

The limits of the Moon's penumbral shadow define the region of visibility of the partial eclipse. This saddle-shaped region often covers more than half of Earth's daylight hemisphere and consists of several distinct zones or limits. At the northern and southern boundaries lie the limits of the penumbra's path. Great loops at the western and eastern extremes of the penumbra's path identify the areas where the eclipse begins and ends at sunrise and sunset, respectively.

Bisecting the *eclipse begins and ends at sunrise and sunset* loops is the curve of maximum eclipse at sunrise (western loop) and sunset (eastern loop). The exterior tangency points *P1* and *P4* mark the coordinates where the penumbral shadow first contacts (partial eclipse begins) and last contacts (partial eclipse ends) Earth's surface. The path of the umbral shadow travels west to east within the penumbral path.

A curve of maximum eclipse is the locus of all points where the eclipse is at maximum at a given time. They are plotted at each half hour in Coordinated Universal Time, and generally run in a north-south direction. The outline of the umbral shadow is plotted every 10 minutes in Coordinated Universal Time. Curves of constant eclipse magnitude[4] delineate the locus of all points where the magnitude at maximum eclipse is constant. These curves run exclusively between the *curves of maximum eclipse at sunrise and sunset*. Furthermore, they are quasi-parallel to the northern and southern penumbral limits. These two limits may be thought of as curves of constant magnitude of 0.0, while the adjacent curves are for magnitudes of 0.2, 0.4, 0.6, and 0.8. The northern and southern limits of the path of total eclipse are curves of constant magnitude of 1.0.

Data pertinent to the eclipse also appear with the orthographic map in Figure 1–1. At the top is the instant of greatest eclipse, expressed in Terrestrial Time and Coordinated Universal Time. The eclipse magnitude is the geocentric ratio of diameters of the Moon and the Sun. Gamma is the minimum distance of the Moon's shadow axis from Earth's center in Earth radii at greatest eclipse. Finally, the Saros series of the eclipse is listed, followed by the Saros Member position. The first number identifies the sequence position of the eclipse in the Saros, while the second is the total number of eclipses in the series.

---

2 The instant of greatest eclipse occurs when the distance between the Moon's shadow axis and Earth's center reaches a minimum.

3 The sub-solar point is the geographic location where the Sun appears directly overhead (zenith).

4 Eclipse magnitude is defined as the fraction of the Sun's diameter occulted by the Moon. It is strictly a ratio of diameters and should not be confused with eclipse obscuration, which is a measure of the Sun's surface area occulted by the Moon. Eclipse magnitude is usually expressed as a decimal fraction (e.g., 0.50) but can also appear as a percentage (e.g., 50%).

In the upper left and right corners are the geocentric coordinates of the Sun and the Moon, respectively, at the instant of greatest eclipse. They are:

R.A. – Right Ascension
Dec. – Declination
S.D. – Apparent Semi-Diameter
H.P. – Horizontal Parallax

To the lower left are exterior/interior contact times of the Moon's penumbral shadow with Earth, which are defined:

P1 – Instant of first exterior tangency of Penumbra with Earth's limb. (Partial Eclipse Begins)
P2 – Instant of first interior tangency of Penumbra with Earth's limb.
P3 – Instant of last interior tangency of Penumbra with Earth's limb.
P4 – Instant of last exterior tangency of Penumbra with Earth's limb. (Partial Eclipse Ends)

The lower right corner lists exterior/interior contact times of the Moon's umbral shadow with Earth's limb which are defined as follows:

U1 – Instant of first exterior tangency of Umbra with Earth's limb.
(Umbral [Total] Eclipse Begins)
U2 – Instant of first interior tangency of Umbra with Earth's limb.
U3 – Instant of last interior tangency of Umbra with Earth's limb.
U4 – Instant of last exterior tangency of Umbra with Earth's limb.
(Umbral [Total] Eclipse Ends)

At bottom left are the geographic coordinates of the position of greatest eclipse along with the local circumstances at that location (i.e., Sun altitude, Sun azimuth, path width and duration of totality).

At bottom right are the corresponding values for the position of greatest duration. Although the geographic locations of greatest duration and greatest eclipse differ by about 95 km (59 miles) and 2 ¼ minutes along the eclipse track, the difference in the duration of totality is less than 0.06 second which is of no practical consequence.

1.3 Stereographic Projection Map of the Eclipse Path

The stereographic projection of Earth in Figure 1–2 depicts the paths of penumbral and umbral (total) eclipses. These paths cover a wide range of longitudes and latitudes, wrapping nearly half way around the globe. The stereographic projection is particularly useful for illustrating the sunrise/sunset regions of the path that are badly foreshortened in the orthographic projection used in Figure 1–1. Of course, the stereographic projection has its own shortcomings — it preserves neither distances nor the areas of continents, especially as the distance from the origin increases.

Figure 1–2 is oriented with north at the top. International political borders are shown and circles of latitude and longitude are plotted at 30° increments. The region of penumbral or partial eclipse is identified by its northern and southern limits, the curves of *eclipse begins/ends at sunrise/sunset*, and curves of *maximum eclipse at sunrise/sunset*, all of which are identified. Curves of *constant eclipse magnitude* are plotted for magnitudes 0.20, 0.40, 0.60, and 0.80, as are the limits of the path of total eclipse. Also included are curves of greatest eclipse at every half hour Coordinated Universal Time.

1.4 Equidistant Conic Projection Map of the Eclipse Path

Figure 1–3 uses an equidistant conic projection chosen to minimize distortion, and that isolates the umbral path through Mexico, the United States, and Canada. A number of cities are plotted, as are state and province borders. Curves of maximum eclipse and constant eclipse magnitude are plotted and labeled at intervals of 30 min and 0.1 magnitudes, respectively. A linear scale is included for estimating approximate distances (in kilometers). Within the northern and southern limits of the path of totality, the outline of the umbral shadow is plotted at intervals of 10 minutes. The duration of totality (minutes and seconds) and the Sun's altitude correspond to the local circumstances on the central line at each shadow position.

Figures 1–1, 1–2 and 1–3 may be used to quickly determine the approximate time and magnitude of maximum eclipse at any location within the eclipse path.

Figure 1–2: Stereographic Projection Map of 2024 Eclipse Path

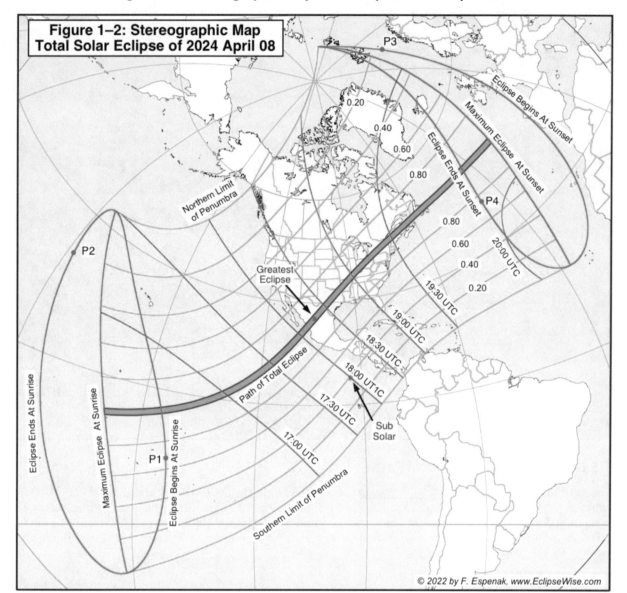

Photo 1–2: The diamond ring effect at second and third contact frame an image of the corona during totality. Casper, Wyoming, 2017 August 21.

Figure 1–3: Equidistant Conic Projection Map of 2024 Eclipse Path

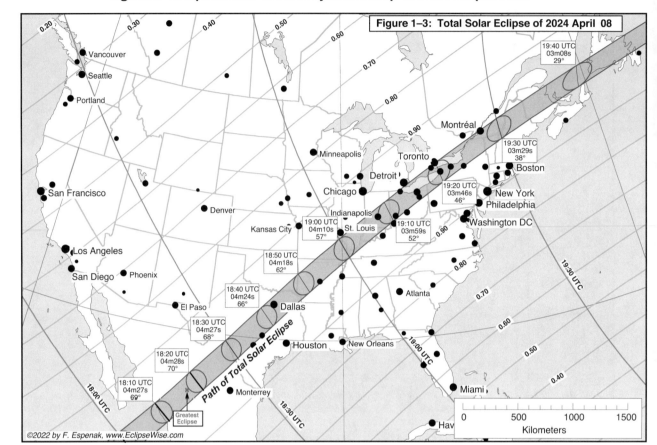

1.5 Description of the Umbral Path

The path of the Moon's umbral shadow begins at 16:40 UTC[5] in the South Pacific about 3300 km (2060 mi) south of the Hawaiian Islands and 1390 km (866 mi) northwest of Tahiti. Along the sunrise terminator, the maximum duration is 2 min 6 sec (i.e., 2 minutes 6 seconds) as seen from the center of the narrow, 144 km (89 mi) wide path. No major landfall occurs during the first eighty-five minutes of the central eclipse as the shadow sweeps northeast across the Pacific.

The umbra finally meets terra firma among the Islas Marias at 18:05 UTC (11:05 MST). This archipelago lies about 100 km (62 mi) off the western coast of Mexico. Isla Maria Madre is completely inside the path while Isla Maria Magdalena is bisected by the path's southern limit. Five minutes later (18:10 UTC; 11:10 MST), the umbra reaches Mexico's Pacific coast in the state of Nayarit.

The central line duration of totality here is 4 min 27 sec and the Sun stands 69° above the horizon. The path width has expanded to 199 km (124 mi) as the shadow pursues its

---

5 UTC or Coordinated Universal Time is the primary time standard that regulates world clocks and time. It is based on International Atomic Time (TAI) with leap seconds added at irregular intervals to compensate for the slowing of Earth's rotation. Leap seconds keep UTC within 0.9 second of UT1 (UT1 is mean solar time at 0° longitude). UTC is not adjusted for daylight saving time. It is effectively a successor to Greenwich Mean Time (GMT).

eastward track with a ground velocity of 0.70 km/s (1566 mi/hr). This is twice the speed of sound (0.34 km/s or 760 mi/hr).

Mazatlan, a major resort city known for its beaches and warm, sunny weather, is 26 km (16 mi) northwest of the central line. Its population of 500,000 will experience 4 min 16 sec of totality. Many eclipse chasers will be attracted by the long duration and promising weather prospects of this destination.

After crossing a relatively narrow (25 km) coastal plain, the path climbs over the Sierra Madre Occidental (2600 m) and enters the Mexican Plateau (1100 m) consisting of desert plains and low mountain ridges. Durango lies about 55 km (34 mi) south of the central line but still manages 3 min 47 sec of totality.

The umbra reaches the point of greatest eclipse at 18:17:20 UTC (12:17:20 CST) about 150 km (93 mi) northeast of Durango. The duration of totality is 4 min 28 sec with a Sun altitude of 70°. The point of greatest duration is located 95 km (59 mi) northeast but only exceeds the duration of greatest eclipse by 0.05 seconds.

Climbing over the Sierra Madre Oriental (1500 m), the lunar shadow descends into the lowlands of the Gulf Coastal Plains. Piedras Negras (pop. 164,000) stands on the south side of the Rio Grande 14 km (9 mi) southeast of the central line. Totality lasts 4 min 24 sec.

The umbral shadow crosses the Rio Grande and enters Texas at 18:30 UTC (13:30 CDT). Although the central duration is beginning to decrease it still offers a generous 4 min 27 sec of totality.

The eclipse track crosses Texas from the southwest to the northeast. Among the larger cities in the path are San Antonio (on the southern limit), Austin (1 min 43 sec), Waco (4 min 12 sec), Dallas (3 min 51 sec), Fort Worth (2 min 32 sec), and Texarkana (2 min 22 sec). Houston, the largest city in Texas (pop. 2.3 million), is located 200 km (125 mi) outside the path and experiences a partial eclipse with a magnitude of 0.943.

Approximately 12.8 million people live in the eclipse path through Texas. In comparison, the population living within the entire path through the USA is approximately 31.8 million.

Leaving the Lone Star State the lunar shadow cuts across the southeast corner of Oklahoma. Broken Bow lies 14 km (9 mi) north of the central line and its 160,000 citizens can expect 4 min 17 sec of totality. Approximately half of Arkansas lies within the path including capital city Little Rock, which is located within 18 km (11 mi) of the path's southern limit. Little Rock's 527,000 inhabitants will experience a total eclipse lasting 2 min 26 sec.

The southeastern corner of Missouri falls within the totality track including the Show Me State's Poplar Bluff (pop. 17,000). This "Gateway to the Ozarks" city will receive 4 min 8 sec of totality. Nearby and along the path's southern limit in Missouri, a small meander in the Mississippi River brings a single point bar into the path. The neck of the point bar is the only part of Tennessee (less than 2 square miles) in the entire eclipse path.

Cape Girardeau is Missouri's largest city (pop. 40,100) in the path with a duration of 4 min 6 sec. The central line crosses the Missouri/Illinois border at approximately 19:00 UTC (14:00 CDT). The path width is 186 km (115 mi), the central duration is 4 min 10 sec and the Sun's altitude is 57°. Carbondale,

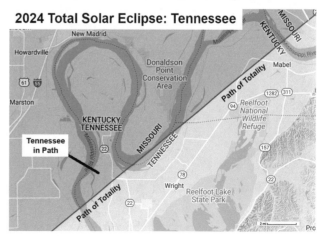

2024 Total Solar Eclipse: Tennessee

IL, the home of Southern Illinois University, experiences it's second total solar eclipse in just 6 ¾ years. It was a major destination for the 2017 eclipse because Carbondale was near the point of greatest eclipse.

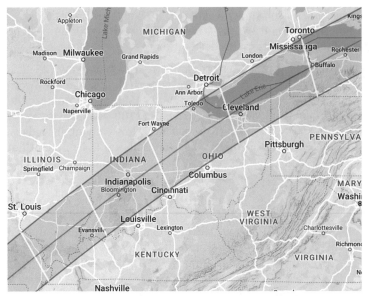

The southern half of Indiana stands in the umbra's path which includes capital city Indianapolis (869,000 pop.). Residents of the Hoosier State's capital will be engulfed by the Moon's shadow for 3 min 48 sec. The path narrowly misses several large cities nearby including Memphis, TN (mag=0.976), St. Louis, MO (mag=0.987), and Louisville, KY (mag=0.989).

To the southeast, the path grazes the western edge of Kentucky along its Mississippi border. The Bluegrass State's largest town in the path is Paducah (pop. 25,000) where totality lasts 1 min 35 sec.

The trajectory of the shadow through Ohio takes it across Toledo (pop. 275,000), Cleveland (pop. 383,000), and Akron (pop. 197,000). Three other Buckeye State cities, Cincinnati (mag=0.994), Columbus (mag=0.996), and Youngstown (mag=0.997), are near misses.

The southeast corner of Michigan barely makes it into the path with a triangular wedge of land bordered by Ohio and Lake Erie. Unfortunately, nearby city Detroit (pop. 672,000) is outside the path and gets a deep partial eclipse of magnitude 0.991.

As the central line crosses Lake Erie, the northwest corner of Pennsylvania enters the shadow. The largest Keystone State city in the path is Erie (pop. 97,000) where totality lasts 3 min 42 sec.

Meanwhile, the northern edge of the path crosses into Ontario. Hamilton (pop. 776,000) stands 10 km (6 mi) inside the northern limit and receives 1 min 43 sec of totality. Deeper in the path, St. Catharines (pop. 421,000) residents get 3 min 16 sec of total eclipse. Unfortunately, Ontario's capital city, Toronto (pop. 6.8 million), lies 9 km (6 mi) outside the path thereby missing totality with a magnitude 0.997 partial eclipse at 19:20 UTC (15:20 EDT).

New York's Buffalo is on the central line bringing it 3 min 45 sec of total eclipse. The path here is 179 km (111 mi) wide and the Sun's altitude is 46°. About 32 km (20 mi) north of Buffalo is world renowned Niagara Falls where totality lasts 3 min 31 sec. Rochester stands on the southern shore of Lake Ontario. Its 206,000 residents will experience 3 min 39 sec of totality. Downtown Syracuse (pop. 143,000) is within 7.5 km (4.5 mi) of the southern limit but still gets a total eclipse lasting 1 min 25 sec. In Canada, the path now runs across southern Quebec. While downtown Quebec City (pop. 542,000) is inside the path, it is located just 7 km (4 mi) from the northern limit. The duration of total eclipse here is 1 min 27 sec.

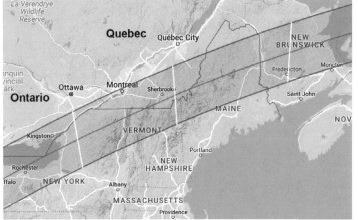

Burlington, the most-populous city in Vermont (pop. 42,600), is located 35 km (22 mi) south of the central line. The duration of totality for this Green

Mountain State city is 3 min 14 sec. Montpelier (pop. 7,400), the state capital, is within 12 km (8 mi) of the southern limit and sees a duration of 1 min 40 sec.

The path continues across northern New Hampshire and Maine, both of which remain rural with no sizable cities. Caribou, ME (pop. 7,700) lies within 16 km (10 mi) of the northern path limit and gets 2 min 10 sec of totality. Located 65 km (40 mi) south of the path, Maine's capital city Augusta (pop. 32,000) gets a partial eclipse of magnitude 0.980.

Exiting the United States (31.8 million live inside the path through the USA), the remainder of the eclipse track runs solely through Canada. The path crosses central New Brunswick where Fredericton, the capital, lies 27 km (17 mi) from the southern limit and receives 2 min 14 sec of total eclipse. Moncton, the largest city in the province (pop. 72,000), is just outside the path and gets a very deep partial eclipse of magnitude 0.998. The path width across New Brunswick is 170 km (106 mi) and the Sun's altitude is 34°.

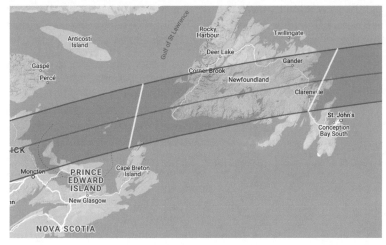

Western Prince Edward Island lies in the path, but Charlottetown (pop. 168,000) is outside where a partial eclipse of magnitude 0.992 occurs. The shadow track then clips the northeastern most tip of Nova Scotia.

Crossing the Gulf of St. Lawrence, Quebec's Magdalen Islands straddle the central line. Last landfall of the umbral shadow is in southern Newfoundland. The late afternoon Sun is only 24° above the horizon. The central line duration is 2 min 54 sec and the path width is 162 km (100 mi). St. John's, the capital, is 42 km (26 mi) south of the path. Its 113,900 inhabitants will get a deep partial eclipse with a magnitude of 0.988.

Leaving Canada with a velocity of 2.08 km/s (4650 mi/hr), the umbra races 2450 km (1550 mi) across the North Atlantic Ocean before reaching the end of the track and returning to space. Over a period of 3 hours 15 minutes, the umbra travels along a 14,800 km (9200 mi) track that covers an area over 0.52% of Earth's surface.

Table 1–0: Population By State in the 2024 Path of Totality

State	Pop. in Path	Last Total Eclipse	Next Total Eclipse
Texas	12784000	1900	2045
Oklahoma	84000	1918	2045
Arkansas	1771000	1918	2045
Missouri	474000	2017	2178
Tennessee	80	2017	2153
Illinois	597000	2017	2153
Kentucky	147000	2017	2153
Indiana	3947000	1869	2099
Ohio	7275000	1806	2099
Michigan	6100	1925	2099
Pennsylvania	433000	1925	2079
New York	3732000	1925	2079
Vermont	399000	1932	2079
New Hampshire	12000	1959	2079
Maine	99000	1963	2079
SUM	31760180	—	—

Population data courtesy of M. Zeiler, 2022 (GreatAmericanEclipse.com)

1.6 Besselian Elements and Eclipse Path Tables

Section 1.6 contains a series of tables that characterize the eclipse and delineate the central umbral path of totality. The geocentric ephemeris for the Sun and Moon, various parameters, constants, and the Besselian elements (polynomial form) are given in Table 1–1. The coordinates of the Sun and the Moon were determined using the JPL DE430 (Jet Propulsion Laboratory Developmental Ephemeris 430). The DE430 is based upon the International Celestial Reference Frame (ICRF), the adopted reference frame of the International Astronomical Union (IAU). It includes the effects of both nutation and libration.

Unless otherwise stated, all predictions are based on center of mass positions for the Moon and Sun with no corrections made for center of figure, lunar limb profile, or atmospheric refraction. The predictions depart from normal International Astronomical Union (IAU) convention through the use of a smaller constant for the mean lunar radius k for all umbral contacts (see Sect. 1.9 "Lunar Limb Profile"). Times are expressed in either Terrestrial Time (TT) or in Coordinated Universal Time (UTC), where TT – UTC = 69.184 seconds (= 32.184 seconds + 37 leap seconds).

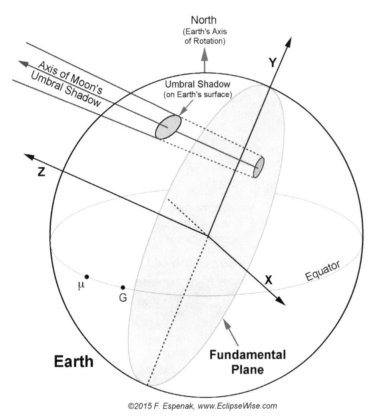

The Fundamental Plane passes through the center of Earth and is perpendicular to the Moon's shadow axis. The Besselian elements for the eclipse are defined with respect to the Fundamental Plane.

The Besselian elements are used to predict all aspects of a solar eclipse. The simplified geometry introduced by Bessel in 1824 transforms the orbital motions of the Sun and Moon into the position, motion, and size of the Moon's penumbral and umbral shadows with respect to a plane passing through Earth. This *fundamental plane* is constructed in an x–y rectangular coordinate system with its origin at Earth's center. The axes are oriented with north in the positive y direction and east in the positive x direction. The z-axis is perpendicular to the plane and parallel to the shadow axis.

The x and y coordinates of the shadow axis are expressed in units of the equatorial radius of Earth. The radii of the penumbral and umbral shadows on the fundamental plane are $l1$ and $l2$, respectively. The direction of the shadow axis on the celestial sphere is defined by its declination d and ephemeris hour angle μ. Finally, the angles that the penumbral and umbral shadow cones make with the shadow axis are expressed as $f1$ and $f2$, respectively.

The details of actual eclipse calculations can be found in the *Explanatory Supplement* (Her Majesty's Nautical Almanac Office 1974) and *Elements of Solar Eclipses* (Meeus 1989).

From the polynomial form of the Besselian elements, any element can be evaluated for any time t_i (in decimal hours) during the eclipse via the equation

$$a = a_0 + a_1\,t + a_2\,t^2 + a_3\,t^3 \qquad (1\text{--}1)$$

$$(\text{or } a = \sum [a_n\,t^n];\ n = 0 \text{ to } 3),$$

where a = x, y, d, $l1$, $l2$, or μ; and t = t_i – t_0 (decimal hours) and t_0 = 18.00 TT (2024 April 08).

The polynomial Besselian elements were derived from a least-squares fit to elements rigorously calculated at five separate times over a 6-hour period centered at t_0.

Table 1–2 lists all external and internal contacts of penumbral and umbral shadows with Earth in UTC.

The contacts are defined:

P1—Instant of first external tangency of penumbral shadow cone with Earth's limb (partial eclipse begins).
P2—Instant of first internal tangency of penumbral shadow cone with Earth's limb.
P3—Instant of last internal tangency of penumbral shadow cone with Earth's limb.
P4—Instant of last external tangency of penumbral shadow cone with Earth's limb (partial eclipse ends).

U1—Instant of first external tangency of umbral shadow cone with Earth's limb (total eclipse begins).
U2—Instant of first internal tangency of umbral shadow cone with Earth's limb.
U3—Instant of last internal tangency of umbral shadow cone with Earth's limb.
U4—Instant of last external tangency of umbral shadow cone with Earth's limb (total eclipse ends).

Similarly, the northern and southern extremes of the penumbral and umbral paths, and extreme limits of the central line are given. The IAU longitude convention is used throughout this publication (i.e., for longitude, east is positive and west is negative; for latitude, north is positive and south is negative).

The path of the umbral shadow is delineated at 5-minute intervals (in Coordinated Universal Time) in Table 1–3. Coordinates of the northern limit, the southern limit, and the central line are listed to the nearest tenth of an arc minute (≈185 m at the Equator). The Sun's altitude, path width, and duration are calculated for the central line position. Table 1–4 presents a physical ephemeris for the umbral shadow at 5-minute intervals in Coordinated Universal Time. The central line coordinates are followed by the topocentric ratio of the apparent diameters of the Moon and Sun, the eclipse obscuration (defined as the fraction of the Sun's surface area occulted by the Moon), and the Sun's altitude and azimuth at that instant. The umbral path width, the umbral shadow's major and minor axes, and its instantaneous velocity with respect to Earth's surface are included. Finally, the central line duration of the total phase is given.

Local circumstances for each central line position, listed in Table 1–3, are presented in Table 1–5. The first three columns give the Coordinated Universal Time of maximum eclipse, the central line duration of totality, and the altitude of the Sun at that instant. The following columns list each of the four eclipse contact times followed by their related contact position angles and the corresponding altitude of the Sun. The four contacts identify significant stages in the progress of the eclipse. They are defined as follows:

First Contact: Instant of first external tangency between the Moon and Sun (partial eclipse begins).
Second Contact: Instant of first internal tangency between the Moon and Sun (total eclipse begins).
Third Contact: Instant of last internal tangency between the Moon and Sun (total eclipse ends).
Fourth Contact: Instant of last external tangency between the Moon and Sun (partial eclipse ends).

Major Contacts for a Total Solar Eclipse

First Contact	Second Contact	Third Contact	Fourth Contact
(partial eclipse begins)	*(total eclipse begins)*	*(total eclipse ends)*	*(partial eclipse ends)*

©2015 F. Espenak, www.EclipseWise.com

The position angles P and V (P is defined as the contact angle measured counterclockwise from the equatorial north point of the Sun's disk, and V is defined as the contact angle measured counterclockwise from the local zenith point of the Sun's disk) identify the point along the Sun's disk where each contact occurs. Second and third contact altitudes are omitted because they are always within 1° of the altitude at maximum eclipse.

Table 1–6 presents topocentric values from the umbral path at maximum eclipse for the Moon's horizontal parallax, semi-diameter, relative angular velocity with respect to the Sun, and libration in longitude. The altitude and azimuth of the Sun are given along with the azimuth of the umbral path. The northern limit position angle identifies the point on the lunar disk defining the umbral path's northern limit. It is measured counterclockwise from the equatorial north point of the Moon. In addition, corrections to the path limits due to the lunar limb profile are listed (minutes of arc in latitude).

The irregular profile of the Moon results in a zone of "grazing eclipse" at each limit, which is delineated by interior and exterior contacts of lunar features with the Sun's limb. This geometry is described in greater detail in the Sect. 1.11 "Limb Corrections to the Path Limits: Graze Zones." Corrections to central line durations due to the lunar limb profile are also included. When added to the durations in Tables 1–3, 1–4, 1–5, and 1–7, a slightly longer central total phase is predicted along the path because of several high mountainous regions along the Moon's eastern and western limbs.

To aid and assist in the plotting of the umbral path on large scale maps, the path coordinates are also tabulated at 0.5° intervals in longitude in Tables 1–7a and 1–7b. The latitude of the northern limit, southern limit, and central line for each longitude is tabulated to the nearest hundredth of an arc minute (≈18.5 m at the Equator) along with the Coordinated Universal Time of maximum eclipse at the central line position. Finally, local circumstances on the central line at maximum eclipse are listed and include the Sun's altitude and azimuth, the umbral path width, and the central duration of totality.

For those wishing to observe from the zones of grazing eclipse, supplemental web-based tables 1-8a through 1-8e list the coordinates of the grazing eclipse zones at 7.5′ intervals in longitude. The time of maximum eclipse is given at both northern and southern limits, as well as the path's azimuth. The elevation and scale factors are also given (see Sect. 1.11 "Limb Corrections to the Path Limits: Graze Zones").

These tables are available at: *www.eclipsewise.com/news/2024.html*

Photo 1–3: A time lapse captures the total eclipse from start to finish. Casper, Wyoming, 2017 August 21.
© 2017 F. Espenak, www.MrEclipse.com

Table 1–1: Elements of the Total Solar Eclipse of 2024 April 08

```
Equatorial Conjunction:      18:37:18.88  TT     J.D. = 2460409.2759130
  (Sun & Moon in R.A.)      (=18:36:09.70  UTC)

Ecliptic Conjunction:        18:22:00.82  TT     J.D. = 2460409.2652873
(Sun & Moon in Ec. Lo.)     (=18:20:51.64  UTC)

     Instant of             18:18:29.41  TT     J.D. = 2460409.2628404
  Greatest Eclipse:         (=18:17:20.23  UTC)
```

Geocentric Coordinates of Sun & Moon at Greatest Eclipse (JPL DE430)

```
Sun:        R.A. = 01h11m36.893s      Moon:        R.A. = 01h10m57.476s
            Dec. = +07°35'29.39"                   Dec. = +07°53'55.47"
Semi-Diameter =       15'58.19"       Semi-Diameter =        16'36.33"
Eq.Hor.Par. =         08.78"          Eq.Hor.Par. =          00'56.61"
    Δ R.A. =          9.179s/h            Δ R.A. =           134.758s/h
    Δ Dec. =          55.82"/h            Δ Dec. =           1045.30"/h

Lunar Radius   k1 = 0.2725076 (Penumbra)      Shift in      Δb =  0.00"
Constants:     k2 = 0.2722810 (Umbra)     Lunar Position:   Δl =  0.00"

Geocentric Libration:   l =   1.97°      Brown Lun. No. =  1253
 (Optical+Physical)     b =  -0.44°      Saros Series =  139 (30/71)
                        c = -20.74°           nDot = -25.820 "/cy**2

Eclipse Magnitude = 1.05656       Gamma = 0.34314       TT-UTC = 69.18 s
```

Polynomial Besselian Elements for: 2024 Apr 08   18:00:00 TT (=t_0)

n	x	y	d	l_1	l_2	μ
0	-0.3182485	0.2197639	7.5861838	0.5358323	-0.0102736	89.591230
1	0.5117099	0.2709581	0.0148444	0.0000618	0.0000615	15.004082
2	0.0000326	-0.0000594	-0.0000017	-0.0000128	-0.0000127	-0.000001
3	-0.0000084	-0.0000047	0.0000000	0.0000000	0.0000000	0.000000

$$\text{Tan } f_1 = 0.0046683 \qquad \text{Tan } f_2 = 0.0046450$$

At time t_1 (decimal hours), each Besselian element is evaluated by:

$$x = x_0 + x_1 * t + x_2 * t^2 + x_3 * t^3 \quad (\text{or } x = \Sigma(x_n * t^n); \; n = 0 \text{ to } 3)$$

where: $t = t_1 - t_0$ (decimal hours), and $t_0 = 18.000$

The Besselian elements were derived from a least-squares fit elements calculated at five uniformly spaced times over a 6-hour period centered at t_0. Thus, they are valid over the interval $15.00 \le t0 \le 21.00$ TT.

All times are expressed in Terrestrial Time (TT).

This eclipse is a member of Saros 139. It is the 30th of 71 eclipses in series and occurs near the Moon's Ascending Node.

Table 1–2: Shadow Contacts and Circumstances

```
                              UTC           Latitude      Longitude
                            h  m   s
External/Internal
Contacts of Penumbra:   P1  15:42:14.1    14°57.7'S     143°06.6'W
                        P2  17:45:00.0    19°45.3'N     178°34.8'W
                        P3  18:49:14.7    74°10.7'N     016°10.7'E
                        P4  20:52:21.2    40°33.0'N     036°06.6'W
Extreme
North/South Limits
of Penumbral Path:      N1  17:29:30.9    33°32.2'N     177°01.6'W
                        S1  16:32:23.8    38°45.0'S     151°33.9'W
                        N2  19:04:34.8    82°23.6'N     072°20.7'E
                        S2  20:02:26.8    16°46.7'N     027°54.0'W
External/Internal
Contacts of Umbra:      U1  16:38:51.5    08°02.1'S     158°13.5'W
                        U2  16:41:08.9    07°36.1'S     158°51.4'W
                        U3  19:53:21.2    47°49.9'N     019°26.9'W
                        U4  19:55:36.5    47°24.7'N     020°08.2'W
Extreme
North/South Limits
of Umbral Path:         N1  16:40:27.7    07°11.4'S     158°44.4'W
                        S1  16:39:33.7    08°27.0'S     158°20.7'W
                        N2  19:54:01.5    48°13.9'N     019°29.7'W
                        S2  19:54:55.3    47°00.6'N     020°05.0'W
Extreme Limits
of Central Line:        C1  16:40:00.2    07°49.3'S     158°32.4'W
                        C2  19:54:28.9    47°37.2'N     019°47.6'W
Instant of
Greatest Eclipse:       G0  18:17:20.2    25°17.4'N     104°08.9'W

Instant of
Greatest Duration:      GD  18:19:36.2    25°56.1'N     103°31.3'W
```

```
Circumstances at
Greatest
 Eclipse (GE):   Sun Altitude =  69.8°       Path Width =  197.5 km
                 Sun Azimuth = 149.4°   Central Duration =  04m28.13s

Circumstances at
Greatest
 Duration (GD):  Sun Altitude =  69.7°       Path Width =  197.0 km
                 Sun Azimuth = 153.3°   Central Duration =  04m28.19s

     Distance (GD-GE) =  95.44 km    □ Duration (GD-GE) = 0.0531 s
```

```
 TT - UTC =  69.18 s (= 000°17'20.6" in longitude)
```

Table 1–3: Path of the Umbral Shadow

Universal Time (UTC)	Northern Limit		Southern Limit		Central Line		Sun Alt °	Path Width km	Central Duration
	Latitude	Longitude	Latitude	Longitude	Latitude	Longitude			
Limits	07°11.4'S	158°44.4'W	08°27.0'S	158°20.7'W	07°49.3'S	158°32.4'W	0	144	02m06.3s
16:45	03°50.8'S	143°56.2'W	04°40.4'S	141°36.9'W	04°15.2'S	142°44.9'W	17	168	02m40.6s
16:50	01°36.9'S	138°01.0'W	02°31.5'S	136°04.9'W	02°03.9'S	137°02.1'W	24	177	02m56.2s
16:55	00°21.3'N	133°51.6'W	00°35.7'S	132°04.6'W	00°07.0'S	132°57.6'W	30	184	03m08.6s
17:00	02°11.3'N	130°34.4'W	01°12.7'N	128°52.3'W	01°42.2'N	129°42.9'W	34	189	03m19.2s
17:05	03°56.1'N	127°49.4'W	02°56.3'N	126°10.3'W	03°26.3'N	126°59.5'W	38	193	03m28.5s
17:10	05°37.1'N	125°26.4'W	04°36.3'N	123°49.2'W	05°06.8'N	124°37.5'W	42	196	03m36.8s
17:15	07°15.2'N	123°19.4'W	06°13.7'N	121°43.7'W	06°44.6'N	122°31.3'W	46	199	03m44.3s
17:20	08°51.2'N	121°24.5'W	07°48.8'N	119°49.9'W	08°20.1'N	120°36.9'W	49	200	03m51.1s
17:25	10°25.3'N	119°38.9'W	09°22.2'N	118°05.1'W	09°53.8'N	118°51.8'W	52	201	03m57.2s
17:30	11°57.9'N	118°00.6'W	10°54.0'N	116°27.6'W	11°26.0'N	117°13.8'W	55	202	04m02.7s
17:35	13°29.2'N	116°27.9'W	12°24.6'N	114°55.6'W	12°57.0'N	115°41.5'W	57	202	04m07.6s
17:40	14°59.6'N	114°59.7'W	13°54.1'N	113°28.0'W	14°26.9'N	114°13.6'W	60	202	04m12.0s
17:45	16°29.0'N	113°34.8'W	15°22.7'N	112°03.7'W	15°55.9'N	112°49.1'W	62	202	04m15.8s
17:50	17°57.7'N	112°12.4'W	16°50.6'N	110°41.9'W	17°24.2'N	111°27.0'W	64	202	04m19.1s
17:55	19°25.8'N	110°51.6'W	18°17.7'N	109°21.8'W	18°51.8'N	110°06.5'W	66	201	04m21.9s
18:00	20°53.4'N	109°31.6'W	19°44.2'N	108°02.6'W	20°18.8'N	108°46.9'W	67	200	04m24.2s
18:05	22°20.5'N	108°11.9'W	21°10.2'N	106°43.7'W	21°45.4'N	107°27.6'W	68	199	04m26.0s
18:10	23°47.3'N	106°51.8'W	22°35.8'N	105°24.4'W	23°11.5'N	106°07.9'W	69	198	04m27.2s
18:15	25°13.8'N	105°30.5'W	24°01.0'N	104°04.2'W	24°37.4'N	104°47.2'W	69	198	04m28.0s
18:20	26°40.0'N	104°07.4'W	25°25.9'N	102°42.3'W	26°02.9'N	103°24.7'W	69	196	04m28.2s
18:25	28°06.0'N	102°41.8'W	26°50.5'N	101°18.1'W	27°28.2'N	101°59.8'W	69	195	04m27.9s
18:30	29°31.9'N	101°13.0'W	28°14.8'N	099°51.0'W	28°53.3'N	100°31.8'W	68	194	04m27.0s
18:35	30°57.6'N	099°40.2'W	29°38.9'N	098°20.0'W	30°18.1'N	099°00.0'W	67	193	04m25.6s
18:40	32°23.1'N	098°02.5'W	31°02.7'N	096°44.5'W	31°42.8'N	097°23.4'W	65	192	04m23.7s
18:45	33°48.5'N	096°18.8'W	32°26.4'N	095°03.5'W	33°07.3'N	095°41.1'W	64	190	04m21.2s
18:50	35°13.8'N	094°28.1'W	33°49.8'N	093°15.9'W	34°31.6'N	093°52.0'W	62	189	04m18.1s
18:55	36°38.8'N	092°29.1'W	35°12.9'N	091°20.5'W	35°55.7'N	091°54.8'W	59	187	04m14.4s
19:00	38°03.4'N	090°20.1'W	36°35.6'N	089°15.9'W	37°19.4'N	089°48.0'W	57	186	04m10.0s
19:05	39°27.7'N	087°59.2'W	37°57.9'N	087°00.2'W	38°42.6'N	087°29.8'W	54	184	04m05.1s
19:10	40°51.3'N	085°24.1'W	39°19.6'N	084°31.4'W	40°05.3'N	084°57.9'W	51	182	03m59.4s
19:15	42°13.9'N	082°31.9'W	40°40.5'N	081°46.7'W	41°27.0'N	082°09.5'W	48	180	03m53.1s
19:20	43°35.3'N	079°18.6'W	42°00.1'N	078°42.6'W	42°47.5'N	079°01.0'W	45	178	03m46.0s
19:25	44°54.7'N	075°39.2'W	43°18.1'N	075°14.5'W	44°06.2'N	075°27.4'W	42	176	03m38.0s
19:30	46°11.3'N	071°26.3'W	44°33.5'N	071°15.9'W	45°22.2'N	071°21.8'W	38	173	03m29.1s
19:35	47°23.6'N	066°29.1'W	45°45.3'N	066°37.1'W	46°34.2'N	066°34.1'W	34	170	03m19.2s
19:40	48°28.9'N	060°29.6'W	46°51.3'N	061°02.3'W	47°40.0'N	060°47.5'W	29	166	03m07.8s
19:45	49°22.2'N	052°53.0'W	47°47.4'N	054°02.1'W	48°34.8'N	053°29.8'W	23	162	02m54.4s
19:50	49°49.5'N	042°04.8'W	48°23.4'N	044°22.4'W	49°06.7'N	043°18.1'W	16	156	02m37.4s
Limits	48°13.9'N	019°29.7'W	47°00.6'N	020°05.0'W	47°37.2'N	019°47.6'W	0	141	02m04.2s

Table 1–4: Physical Elements of the Umbral Shadow

Coordinated Universal Time	Central Line Latitude	Central Line Longitude	Moon/Sun Diameter Ratio	Eclipse Obscur.	Sun Alt °	Sun Azm °	Path Width km	Major Axis km	Minor Axis km	Umbra Veloc. km/s	Central Duration
16:40.0	07°49.3'S	158°32.4'W	1.0395	1.0806	0.0	82.4	144.0	–	132.4	–	02m06.3s
16:45	04°15.2'S	142°44.9'W	1.0450	1.0919	17.3	80.7	168.2	504.3	149.9	2.801	02m40.6s
16:50	02°03.9'S	137°02.1'W	1.0471	1.0965	24.5	80.7	177.8	377.9	156.7	1.891	02m56.2s
16:55	00°07.0'S	132°57.6'W	1.0487	1.0998	30.1	81.2	184.7	322.9	161.8	1.499	03m08.6s
17:00	01°42.2'N	129°42.9'W	1.0500	1.1024	34.8	82.0	189.8	290.6	165.8	1.274	03m19.2s
17:05	03°26.3'N	126°59.5'W	1.0510	1.1047	38.9	83.0	193.8	269.1	169.1	1.126	03m28.5s
17:10	05°06.8'N	124°37.5'W	1.0519	1.1066	42.7	84.4	196.8	253.6	172.0	1.022	03m36.8s
17:15	06°44.6'N	122°31.3'W	1.0527	1.1082	46.2	86.1	199.0	241.8	174.5	0.945	03m44.3s
17:20	08°20.1'N	120°36.9'W	1.0534	1.1097	49.4	88.1	200.6	232.7	176.6	0.886	03m51.1s
17:25	09°53.8'N	118°51.8'W	1.0540	1.1109	52.4	90.4	201.7	225.4	178.5	0.840	03m57.2s
17:30	11°26.0'N	117°13.8'W	1.0545	1.1120	55.1	93.2	202.4	219.5	180.1	0.804	04m02.7s
17:35	12°57.0'N	115°41.5'W	1.0550	1.1130	57.7	96.4	202.7	214.6	181.5	0.776	04m07.6s
17:40	14°26.9'N	114°13.6'W	1.0554	1.1138	60.1	100.1	202.7	210.7	182.7	0.753	04m12.0s
17:45	15°55.9'N	112°49.1'W	1.0557	1.1145	62.3	104.4	202.4	207.4	183.7	0.736	04m15.8s
17:50	17°24.2'N	111°27.0'W	1.0560	1.1150	64.3	109.4	202.0	204.8	184.6	0.722	04m19.1s
17:55	18°51.8'N	110°06.5'W	1.0562	1.1155	66.0	115.2	201.4	202.7	185.3	0.712	04m21.9s
18:00	20°18.8'N	108°46.9'W	1.0563	1.1159	67.5	121.7	200.7	201.1	185.8	0.704	04m24.2s
18:05	21°45.4'N	107°27.6'W	1.0565	1.1161	68.6	129.0	199.9	199.9	186.2	0.700	04m26.0s
18:10	23°11.5'N	106°07.9'W	1.0565	1.1163	69.4	136.9	199.0	199.1	186.4	0.698	04m27.2s
18:15	24°37.4'N	104°47.2'W	1.0566	1.1163	69.8	145.4	198.0	198.7	186.5	0.698	04m28.0s
18:20	26°02.9'N	103°24.7'W	1.0565	1.1163	69.7	154.0	197.0	198.7	186.4	0.701	04m28.2s
18:25	27°28.2'N	101°59.8'W	1.0565	1.1161	69.3	162.5	195.9	199.0	186.2	0.706	04m27.9s
18:30	28°53.3'N	100°31.8'W	1.0564	1.1159	68.5	170.7	194.7	199.7	185.8	0.714	04m27.0s
18:35	30°18.1'N	099°00.0'W	1.0562	1.1155	67.3	178.3	193.5	200.8	185.3	0.725	04m25.6s
18:40	31°42.8'N	097°23.4'W	1.0560	1.1151	65.8	185.3	192.2	202.4	184.7	0.738	04m23.7s
18:45	33°07.3'N	095°41.1'W	1.0557	1.1146	64.0	191.7	190.9	204.4	183.8	0.754	04m21.2s
18:50	34°31.6'N	093°52.0'W	1.0554	1.1139	62.0	197.6	189.4	206.9	182.9	0.775	04m18.1s
18:55	35°55.7'N	091°54.8'W	1.0550	1.1131	59.8	203.0	187.9	210.1	181.7	0.800	04m14.4s
19:00	37°19.4'N	089°48.0'W	1.0546	1.1122	57.4	208.0	186.3	214.0	180.4	0.829	04m10.0s
19:05	38°42.6'N	087°29.8'W	1.0541	1.1112	54.8	212.7	184.6	218.8	178.8	0.866	04m05.1s
19:10	40°05.3'N	084°57.9'W	1.0536	1.1100	52.0	217.3	182.7	224.6	177.1	0.910	03m59.4s
19:15	41°27.0'N	082°09.5'W	1.0529	1.1086	49.0	221.8	180.7	231.9	175.0	0.965	03m53.1s
19:20	42°47.5'N	079°01.0'W	1.0522	1.1071	45.7	226.3	178.6	241.1	172.8	1.034	03m46.0s
19:25	44°06.2'N	075°27.4'W	1.0514	1.1053	42.3	230.9	176.1	252.8	170.1	1.122	03m38.0s
19:30	45°22.2'N	071°21.8'W	1.0504	1.1033	38.5	235.7	173.4	268.5	167.1	1.239	03m29.1s
19:35	46°34.2'N	066°34.1'W	1.0493	1.1010	34.3	240.9	170.4	290.5	163.6	1.402	03m19.2s
19:40	47°40.0'N	060°47.5'W	1.0479	1.0982	29.5	246.8	166.8	323.7	159.4	1.649	03m07.8s
19:45	48°34.8'N	053°29.8'W	1.0463	1.0947	23.8	253.7	162.4	381.7	154.1	2.078	02m54.4s
19:50	49°06.7'N	043°18.1'W	1.0440	1.0899	16.3	262.7	156.3	522.3	146.8	3.116	02m37.4s
19:54.5	47°37.2'N	019°47.6'W	1.0388	1.0792	0.0	281.3	142.0	–	130.2	–	02m04.2s

Table 1–5: Local Circumstances on the Central Line

Central Line Maximum Eclipse			First Contact				Second Contact			Third Contact			Fourth Contact			
UTC	Duration	Alt °	UTC	P °	V °	Alt °	UTC	P °	V °	UTC	P °	V °	UTC	P °	V °	Alt °
16:40.0	02m06.3s	1	–	–	–	–	16:38:57	59	157	16:41:03	239	337	17:36:51	57	157	14
16:45	02m40.6s	17	15:47:01	237	331	3	16:43:40	55	152	16:46:21	235	332	17:49:08	53	153	33
16:50	02m56.2s	25	15:49:21	235	328	10	16:48:32	53	149	16:51:28	233	329	17:57:21	51	150	41
16:55	03m08.6s	30	15:52:15	234	326	15	16:53:26	52	146	16:56:35	232	326	18:04:50	49	148	47
17:00	03m19.2s	35	15:55:25	233	323	19	16:58:21	50	144	17:01:40	230	324	18:11:54	48	145	53
17:05	03m28.5s	39	15:58:48	232	321	23	17:03:16	49	141	17:06:45	229	321	18:18:40	47	143	57
17:10	03m36.8s	43	16:02:20	231	319	26	17:08:12	49	139	17:11:49	228	319	18:25:12	46	140	61
17:15	03m44.3s	46	16:05:59	230	316	29	17:13:08	48	136	17:16:52	228	316	18:31:33	46	136	65
17:20	03m51.1s	49	16:09:45	229	314	32	17:18:05	47	133	17:21:56	227	313	18:37:44	45	132	69
17:25	03m57.2s	52	16:13:36	229	312	35	17:23:02	47	130	17:26:59	226	310	18:43:45	45	126	72
17:30	04m02.7s	55	16:17:32	228	310	37	17:27:59	46	127	17:32:02	226	307	18:49:39	44	119	75
17:35	04m07.6s	58	16:21:33	228	307	40	17:32:57	46	124	17:37:04	226	303	18:55:25	44	110	77
17:40	04m12.0s	60	16:25:39	227	305	42	17:37:54	45	120	17:42:06	225	299	19:01:03	44	97	79
17:45	04m15.8s	62	16:29:49	227	302	45	17:42:52	45	116	17:47:08	225	295	19:06:35	44	82	79
17:50	04m19.1s	64	16:34:03	226	299	47	17:47:51	45	111	17:52:10	225	290	19:12:00	44	65	80
17:55	04m21.9s	66	16:38:22	226	296	49	17:52:49	45	105	17:57:11	225	284	19:17:18	44	50	79
18:00	04m24.2s	67	16:42:44	226	293	51	17:57:48	45	99	18:02:12	225	278	19:22:31	44	38	77
18:05	04m26.0s	69	16:47:11	226	290	52	18:02:47	45	93	18:07:13	225	271	19:27:37	45	30	75
18:10	04m27.2s	69	16:51:42	226	286	54	18:07:47	45	86	18:12:14	225	263	19:32:37	45	23	73
18:15	04m28.0s	70	16:56:18	226	283	56	18:12:46	45	78	18:17:14	225	256	19:37:31	45	19	71
18:20	04m28.2s	70	17:00:58	226	278	57	18:17:46	45	70	18:22:14	225	248	19:42:19	46	16	68
18:25	04m27.9s	69	17:05:43	226	274	58	18:22:46	46	63	18:27:14	226	240	19:47:01	46	13	66
18:30	04m27.0s	68	17:10:33	226	269	59	18:27:47	46	56	18:32:14	226	233	19:51:37	47	12	63
18:35	04m25.6s	67	17:15:27	226	264	60	18:32:47	46	49	18:37:13	226	227	19:56:07	47	11	61
18:40	04m23.7s	66	17:20:28	227	259	61	18:37:48	47	43	18:42:12	227	221	20:00:31	48	10	58
18:45	04m21.2s	64	17:25:34	227	253	61	18:42:49	47	39	18:47:11	228	217	20:04:49	49	10	56
18:50	04m18.1s	62	17:30:46	228	248	61	18:47:51	48	34	18:52:09	228	213	20:09:02	50	10	53
18:55	04m14.4s	60	17:36:05	228	242	61	18:52:53	49	31	18:57:07	229	209	20:13:08	50	10	50
19:00	04m10.0s	57	17:41:31	229	236	60	18:57:55	50	28	19:02:05	230	207	20:17:08	51	10	47
19:05	04m05.1s	55	17:47:05	229	231	59	19:02:57	50	26	19:07:02	230	204	20:21:01	52	10	44
19:10	03m59.4s	52	17:52:47	230	226	57	19:08:00	51	24	19:12:00	231	203	20:24:48	53	11	41
19:15	03m53.1s	49	17:58:38	231	221	56	19:13:03	52	22	19:16:56	232	201	20:28:28	54	12	38
19:20	03m46.0s	46	18:04:39	232	217	53	19:18:07	53	21	19:21:53	233	200	20:32:01	55	13	35
19:25	03m38.0s	42	18:10:52	233	214	51	19:23:11	54	20	19:26:49	234	200	20:35:26	56	14	31
19:30	03m29.1s	38	18:17:18	234	210	48	19:28:15	56	20	19:31:44	236	199	20:38:41	57	15	28
19:35	03m19.2s	34	18:24:01	235	208	44	19:33:20	57	19	19:36:39	237	199	20:41:46	58	16	24
19:40	03m07.8s	30	18:31:03	237	205	39	19:38:26	58	20	19:41:34	238	199	20:44:36	60	18	19
19:45	02m54.4s	24	18:38:34	238	203	34	19:43:33	60	20	19:46:27	240	200	20:47:05	61	19	14
19:50	02m37.4s	16	18:46:56	240	202	26	19:48:41	62	21	19:51:19	242	201	20:48:55	63	22	7
19:54.5	02m04.2s	1	18:58:23	244	201	9	19:53:27	65	23	19:55:31	245	203	–	–	–	–

Table 1–6: Topocentric Data and Path Corrections Due to Lunar Limb Profile

Universal Time (UTC)	Moon Topo H.P. "	Moon Topo S.D. "	Moon Rel. Ang.V "/s	Topo Lib. Long °	Sun Alt °	Sun Azm °	Path Azm °	North Limit P.A. °	Limit Int. ′	Limit Ext. ′	Limit Int. ′	Limit Ext. ′	Central Durat. Cor. s
16:45	3677.2	1001.3	0.537	2.79	17.3	80.7	71.5	324.8	-0.3	1.1	0.7	-2.8	0.8
16:50	3684.9	1003.4	0.512	2.75	24.5	80.7	66.4	323.0	-0.6	1.1	0.5	-2.4	1.1
16:55	3690.5	1004.9	0.495	2.71	30.1	81.2	62.4	321.6	-0.9	1.3	0.3	-2.8	0.8
17:00	3695.0	1006.1	0.481	2.66	34.8	82.0	59.0	320.4	-1.2	1.5	0.1	-3.7	0.7
17:05	3698.8	1007.1	0.469	2.62	39.0	83.0	56.0	319.4	-1.4	1.4	-0.2	-4.1	0.6
17:10	3702.0	1008.0	0.459	2.58	42.7	84.4	53.3	318.5	-1.6	1.0	-0.2	-4.5	0.4
17:15	3704.8	1008.8	0.451	2.54	46.2	86.1	50.9	317.8	-1.7	0.9	-0.3	-4.9	0.3
17:20	3707.3	1009.4	0.443	2.50	49.4	88.1	48.9	317.1	-1.9	1.1	-0.4	-5.0	0.2
17:25	3709.4	1010.0	0.437	2.45	52.4	90.4	47.0	316.5	-2.0	1.2	-0.5	-5.0	0.2
17:30	3711.2	1010.5	0.431	2.41	55.2	93.2	45.4	316.1	-2.1	1.1	-0.6	-4.9	0.2
17:35	3712.8	1010.9	0.426	2.37	57.8	96.4	44.1	315.7	-2.2	1.0	-0.6	-4.7	0.3
17:40	3714.2	1011.3	0.421	2.33	60.1	100.1	43.0	315.3	-2.3	1.1	-0.7	-4.7	0.3
17:45	3715.4	1011.6	0.417	2.28	62.3	104.4	42.1	315.1	-2.4	1.2	-0.8	-4.6	0.3
17:50	3716.4	1011.8	0.414	2.24	64.3	109.4	41.4	314.9	-2.4	1.2	-0.8	-4.5	0.3
17:55	3717.1	1012.1	0.411	2.20	66.0	115.2	40.9	314.8	-2.5	1.2	-0.8	-4.4	0.1
18:00	3717.7	1012.2	0.409	2.16	67.5	121.7	40.6	314.8	-2.4	1.2	-0.8	-4.4	0.0
18:05	3718.2	1012.3	0.407	2.11	68.6	129.0	40.5	314.8	-2.4	1.2	-0.8	-4.4	-0.1
18:10	3718.4	1012.4	0.406	2.07	69.4	136.9	40.6	314.9	-2.4	1.2	-0.8	-4.4	-0.1
18:15	3718.5	1012.4	0.405	2.03	69.8	145.4	40.9	315.1	-2.4	1.2	-0.7	-4.5	-0.1
18:20	3718.4	1012.4	0.404	1.99	69.7	154.0	41.3	315.3	-2.3	1.1	-0.7	-4.5	-0.0
18:25	3718.2	1012.3	0.404	1.94	69.3	162.5	42.0	315.6	-2.2	1.0	-0.6	-4.6	0.0
18:30	3717.8	1012.2	0.405	1.90	68.5	170.7	42.8	316.0	-2.1	1.0	-0.5	-4.7	0.1
18:35	3717.2	1012.1	0.406	1.86	67.3	178.3	43.8	316.4	-2.0	1.1	-0.4	-4.8	0.1
18:40	3716.4	1011.9	0.407	1.82	65.8	185.3	45.0	316.9	-1.9	1.1	-0.4	-4.9	0.3
18:45	3715.5	1011.6	0.409	1.77	64.0	191.7	46.3	317.5	-1.7	0.9	-0.3	-4.8	0.5
18:50	3714.3	1011.3	0.412	1.73	62.0	197.6	47.9	318.1	-1.6	0.7	-0.2	-4.5	0.5
18:55	3713.0	1011.0	0.415	1.69	59.8	203.0	49.6	318.8	-1.4	1.0	-0.1	-4.3	0.6
19:00	3711.5	1010.5	0.419	1.64	57.4	208.0	51.5	319.6	-1.2	1.3	-0.1	-4.1	0.7
19:05	3709.7	1010.1	0.423	1.60	54.8	212.7	53.7	320.4	-1.0	1.4	0.1	-3.8	0.7
19:10	3707.7	1009.5	0.429	1.56	52.0	217.3	56.0	321.3	-0.9	1.2	0.3	-3.1	0.7
19:15	3705.4	1008.9	0.435	1.52	49.0	221.8	58.6	322.3	-0.7	0.8	0.5	-2.2	0.6
19:20	3702.8	1008.2	0.443	1.47	45.8	226.3	61.5	323.3	-0.4	1.2	0.6	-2.3	0.6
19:25	3699.8	1007.4	0.452	1.43	42.3	230.9	64.7	324.4	-0.2	1.2	0.7	-2.6	0.4
19:30	3696.4	1006.5	0.462	1.39	38.5	235.7	68.2	325.6	-0.2	0.8	0.8	-2.6	-0.0
19:35	3692.4	1005.4	0.474	1.35	34.3	240.9	72.2	326.9	-0.2	0.5	0.9	-2.4	-0.4
19:40	3687.7	1004.1	0.489	1.31	29.5	246.8	76.7	328.3	-0.2	0.9	1.0	-1.9	-0.6
19:45	3681.8	1002.5	0.509	1.26	23.8	253.7	82.0	329.9	-0.1	0.6	1.0	-0.8	-0.8
19:50	3673.7	1000.3	0.536	1.22	16.4	262.7	88.8	331.8	-0.0	0.7	1.0	-2.0	-0.8

Table 1–7: Mapping Coordinates for the Path of Totality

Longitude	Latitude of:			Circumstances on Central Line				
	Northern Limit	Southern Limit	Central Line	Un. Time (UTC) h m s	Sun Alt °	Sun Az. °	Path Width km	Central Durat.
107°00.0'W	23°38.45'N	20°52.51'N	22°15.39'N	18:06:44	68.9	131.7	199.6	04m26.5s
106°30.0'W	24°10.63'N	21°25.11'N	22°47.81'N	18:08:37	69.2	134.7	199.2	04m26.9s
106°00.0'W	24°42.58'N	21°57.57'N	23°20.05'N	18:10:30	69.4	137.8	198.9	04m27.3s
105°30.0'W	25°14.27'N	22°29.86'N	23°52.07'N	18:12:22	69.6	140.9	198.5	04m27.6s
105°00.0'W	25°45.68'N	23°01.95'N	24°23.85'N	18:14:13	69.7	144.0	198.2	04m27.9s
104°30.0'W	26°16.78'N	23°33.82'N	24°55.36'N	18:16:03	69.8	147.2	197.8	04m28.1s
104°00.0'W	26°47.54'N	24°05.42'N	25°26.58'N	18:17:53	69.8	150.3	197.4	04m28.2s
103°30.0'W	27°17.96'N	24°36.74'N	25°57.47'N	18:19:41	69.7	153.4	197.0	04m28.2s
103°00.0'W	27°48.00'N	25°07.76'N	26°28.02'N	18:21:28	69.6	156.5	196.6	04m28.1s
102°30.0'W	28°17.65'N	25°38.44'N	26°58.21'N	18:23:14	69.5	159.5	196.3	04m28.0s
102°00.0'W	28°46.91'N	26°08.76'N	27°28.01'N	18:24:59	69.3	162.5	195.9	04m27.9s
101°30.0'W	29°15.74'N	26°38.72'N	27°57.42'N	18:26:43	69.0	165.4	195.5	04m27.6s
101°00.0'W	29°44.15'N	27°08.29'N	28°26.43'N	18:28:25	68.8	168.2	195.1	04m27.4s
100°30.0'W	30°12.12'N	27°37.46'N	28°55.01'N	18:30:06	68.4	170.8	194.7	04m27.0s
100°00.0'W	30°39.65'N	28°06.21'N	29°23.16'N	18:31:46	68.1	173.4	194.3	04m26.6s
099°30.0'W	31°06.73'N	28°34.53'N	29°50.87'N	18:33:24	67.7	175.9	193.9	04m26.1s
099°00.0'W	31°33.35'N	29°02.41'N	30°18.13'N	18:35:00	67.3	178.3	193.5	04m25.6s
098°30.0'W	31°59.52'N	29°29.86'N	30°44.94'N	18:36:35	66.8	180.6	193.1	04m25.1s
098°00.0'W	32°25.23'N	29°56.85'N	31°11.29'N	18:38:08	66.4	182.8	192.7	04m24.5s
097°30.0'W	32°50.47'N	30°23.39'N	31°37.19'N	18:39:40	65.9	184.9	192.3	04m23.8s
097°00.0'W	33°15.26'N	30°49.47'N	32°02.62'N	18:41:10	65.4	186.9	191.9	04m23.1s
096°30.0'W	33°39.59'N	31°15.09'N	32°27.60'N	18:42:39	64.9	188.8	191.5	04m22.4s
096°00.0'W	34°03.47'N	31°40.25'N	32°52.11'N	18:44:06	64.4	190.6	191.1	04m21.7s
095°30.0'W	34°26.89'N	32°04.95'N	33°16.17'N	18:45:31	63.8	192.4	190.7	04m20.9s
095°00.0'W	34°49.86'N	32°29.19'N	33°39.78'N	18:46:55	63.3	194.1	190.3	04m20.0s
094°30.0'W	35°12.39'N	32°52.98'N	34°02.93'N	18:48:18	62.7	195.7	189.9	04m19.2s
094°00.0'W	35°34.47'N	33°16.31'N	34°25.63'N	18:49:39	62.2	197.2	189.5	04m18.3s
093°30.0'W	35°56.12'N	33°39.19'N	34°47.90'N	18:50:58	61.6	198.7	189.2	04m17.4s
093°00.0'W	36°17.34'N	34°01.62'N	35°09.72'N	18:52:16	61.0	200.1	188.8	04m16.5s
092°30.0'W	36°38.13'N	34°23.62'N	35°31.11'N	18:53:32	60.5	201.5	188.4	04m15.5s
092°00.0'W	36°58.51'N	34°45.17'N	35°52.07'N	18:54:47	59.9	202.8	188.0	04m14.5s
091°30.0'W	37°18.47'N	35°06.30'N	36°12.61'N	18:56:01	59.3	204.0	187.6	04m13.5s
091°00.0'W	37°38.03'N	35°27.00'N	36°32.73'N	18:57:13	58.8	205.3	187.2	04m12.5s
090°30.0'W	37°57.19'N	35°47.28'N	36°52.44'N	18:58:23	58.2	206.4	186.9	04m11.5s
090°00.0'W	38°15.95'N	36°07.15'N	37°11.76'N	18:59:33	57.6	207.6	186.5	04m10.5s
089°30.0'W	38°34.33'N	36°26.62'N	37°30.67'N	19:00:41	57.0	208.7	186.1	04m09.4s
089°00.0'W	38°52.33'N	36°45.68'N	37°49.20'N	19:01:47	56.5	209.7	185.7	04m08.3s
088°30.0'W	39°09.96'N	37°04.35'N	38°07.34'N	19:02:53	55.9	210.8	185.3	04m07.3s
088°00.0'W	39°27.22'N	37°22.63'N	38°25.10'N	19:03:57	55.3	211.8	185.0	04m06.2s
087°30.0'W	39°44.12'N	37°40.53'N	38°42.50'N	19:05:00	54.8	212.7	184.6	04m05.1s
087°00.0'W	40°00.67'N	37°58.06'N	38°59.53'N	19:06:01	54.2	213.7	184.2	04m04.0s
086°30.0'W	40°16.88'N	38°15.22'N	39°16.21'N	19:07:02	53.7	214.6	183.9	04m02.9s
086°00.0'W	40°32.74'N	38°32.03'N	39°32.54'N	19:08:01	53.1	215.5	183.5	04m01.7s
085°30.0'W	40°48.27'N	38°48.48'N	39°48.52'N	19:08:59	52.6	216.4	183.1	04m00.6s
085°00.0'W	41°03.47'N	39°04.58'N	40°04.17'N	19:09:56	52.0	217.2	182.8	03m59.5s
084°30.0'W	41°18.36'N	39°20.34'N	40°19.48'N	19:10:52	51.5	218.1	182.4	03m58.4s
084°00.0'W	41°32.92'N	39°35.77'N	40°34.48'N	19:11:47	50.9	218.9	182.1	03m57.2s
083°30.0'W	41°47.18'N	39°50.87'N	40°49.15'N	19:12:41	50.4	219.7	181.7	03m56.1s
083°00.0'W	42°01.14'N	40°05.65'N	41°03.51'N	19:13:33	49.9	220.5	181.3	03m55.0s
082°30.0'W	42°14.80'N	40°20.12'N	41°17.57'N	19:14:25	49.3	221.3	181.0	03m53.8s

Table 1–7: Mapping Coordinates for the Path of Totality (continued)

Longitude	Latitude of:			Circumstances on Central Line				
	Northern Limit	Southern Limit	Central Line	Un. Time (UTC) h m s	Sun Alt. °	Sun Az. °	Path Width km	Central Durat.
082°00.0'W	42°28.17'N	40°34.27'N	41°31.33'N	19:15:16	48.8	222.0	180.6	03m52.7s
081°30.0'W	42°41.25'N	40°48.13'N	41°44.79'N	19:16:06	48.3	222.8	180.3	03m51.6s
081°00.0'W	42°54.05'N	41°01.68'N	41°57.96'N	19:16:55	47.8	223.5	179.9	03m50.4s
080°30.0'W	43°06.58'N	41°14.94'N	42°10.85'N	19:17:43	47.2	224.2	179.6	03m49.3s
080°00.0'W	43°18.84'N	41°27.92'N	42°23.47'N	19:18:30	46.7	224.9	179.2	03m48.2s
079°30.0'W	43°30.83'N	41°40.62'N	42°35.80'N	19:19:16	46.2	225.6	178.9	03m47.0s
079°00.0'W	43°42.56'N	41°53.04'N	42°47.88'N	19:20:01	45.7	226.3	178.5	03m45.9s
078°30.0'W	43°54.04'N	42°05.19'N	42°59.68'N	19:20:46	45.2	227.0	178.2	03m44.8s
078°00.0'W	44°05.26'N	42°17.07'N	43°11.24'N	19:21:30	44.7	227.6	177.9	03m43.7s
077°30.0'W	44°16.24'N	42°28.69'N	43°22.53'N	19:22:13	44.2	228.3	177.5	03m42.6s
077°00.0'W	44°26.98'N	42°40.06'N	43°33.58'N	19:22:55	43.7	228.9	177.2	03m41.4s
076°30.0'W	44°37.48'N	42°51.18'N	43°44.39'N	19:23:36	43.3	229.5	176.8	03m40.3s
076°00.0'W	44°47.75'N	43°02.05'N	43°54.95'N	19:24:17	42.8	230.2	176.5	03m39.2s
075°30.0'W	44°57.79'N	43°12.67'N	44°05.28'N	19:24:57	42.3	230.8	176.2	03m38.1s
075°00.0'W	45°07.60'N	43°23.06'N	44°15.38'N	19:25:36	41.8	231.4	175.8	03m37.0s
074°30.0'W	45°17.19'N	43°33.22'N	44°25.25'N	19:26:14	41.3	232.0	175.5	03m35.9s
074°00.0'W	45°26.57'N	43°43.14'N	44°34.89'N	19:26:52	40.9	232.6	175.2	03m34.8s
073°30.0'W	45°35.73'N	43°52.84'N	44°44.32'N	19:27:29	40.4	233.2	174.8	03m33.7s
073°00.0'W	45°44.68'N	44°02.32'N	44°53.53'N	19:28:05	39.9	233.8	174.5	03m32.7s
072°30.0'W	45°53.43'N	44°11.58'N	45°02.53'N	19:28:41	39.5	234.4	174.2	03m31.6s
072°00.0'W	46°01.97'N	44°20.63'N	45°11.32'N	19:29:16	39.0	235.0	173.9	03m30.5s
071°30.0'W	46°10.31'N	44°29.46'N	45°19.91'N	19:29:51	38.6	235.5	173.5	03m29.4s
071°00.0'W	46°18.45'N	44°38.09'N	45°28.29'N	19:30:25	38.1	236.1	173.2	03m28.4s
070°30.0'W	46°26.40'N	44°46.51'N	45°36.47'N	19:30:58	37.7	236.7	172.9	03m27.3s
070°00.0'W	46°34.16'N	44°54.74'N	45°44.46'N	19:31:31	37.2	237.2	172.6	03m26.3s
069°30.0'W	46°41.73'N	45°02.76'N	45°52.26'N	19:32:03	36.8	237.8	172.2	03m25.2s
069°00.0'W	46°49.12'N	45°10.59'N	45°59.86'N	19:32:34	36.4	238.3	171.9	03m24.2s
068°30.0'W	46°56.33'N	45°18.23'N	46°07.28'N	19:33:05	35.9	238.8	171.6	03m23.1s
068°00.0'W	47°03.35'N	45°25.69'N	46°14.52'N	19:33:36	35.5	239.4	171.3	03m22.1s
067°30.0'W	47°10.20'N	45°32.95'N	46°21.58'N	19:34:06	35.0	239.9	171.0	03m21.1s
067°00.0'W	47°16.88'N	45°40.04'N	46°28.45'N	19:34:35	34.6	240.5	170.7	03m20.0s
066°30.0'W	47°23.38'N	45°46.94'N	46°35.15'N	19:35:04	34.2	241.0	170.3	03m19.0s
066°00.0'W	47°29.71'N	45°53.67'N	46°41.68'N	19:35:32	33.8	241.5	170.0	03m18.0s
065°30.0'W	47°35.88'N	46°00.22'N	46°48.04'N	19:36:00	33.3	242.0	169.7	03m17.0s
065°00.0'W	47°41.89'N	46°06.60'N	46°54.23'N	19:36:28	32.9	242.5	169.4	03m16.0s
064°00.0'W	47°53.41'N	46°18.85'N	47°06.11'N	19:37:21	32.1	243.6	168.8	03m14.0s
063°00.0'W	48°04.30'N	46°30.44'N	47°17.34'N	19:38:12	31.3	244.6	168.2	03m12.1s
062°00.0'W	48°14.57'N	46°41.38'N	47°27.95'N	19:39:02	30.5	245.6	167.5	03m10.1s
061°00.0'W	48°24.24'N	46°51.71'N	47°37.94'N	19:39:50	29.6	246.6	166.9	03m08.2s
060°00.0'W	48°33.33'N	47°01.42'N	47°47.34'N	19:40:37	28.8	247.5	166.3	03m06.3s
059°00.0'W	48°41.85'N	47°10.53'N	47°56.15'N	19:41:21	28.1	248.5	165.7	03m04.4s
058°00.0'W	48°49.81'N	47°19.06'N	48°04.39'N	19:42:04	27.3	249.5	165.1	03m02.6s
057°00.0'W	48°57.22'N	47°27.03'N	48°12.08'N	19:42:46	26.5	250.4	164.5	03m00.7s
056°00.0'W	49°04.09'N	47°34.44'N	48°19.22'N	19:43:26	25.7	251.3	163.9	02m58.9s
055°00.0'W	49°10.45'N	47°41.31'N	48°25.82'N	19:44:05	24.9	252.3	163.3	02m57.1s
054°00.0'W	49°16.29'N	47°47.64'N	48°31.91'N	19:44:42	24.2	253.2	162.7	02m55.3s
053°00.0'W	49°21.62'N	47°53.46'N	48°37.48'N	19:45:18	23.4	254.1	162.1	02m53.6s

1.7 Mean Lunar Radius

A fundamental parameter used in the prediction of solar eclipses is the Moon's mean radius k, expressed in units of Earth's equatorial radius. The actual radius of the Moon varies as a function of position angle and libration due to the irregularity of the lunar limb profile. From 1968 through 1980, the Nautical Almanac Office used two separate values for k in their eclipse predictions. The larger value (k=0.2724880), representing a mean over lunar topographic features, was used for all penumbral (i.e., exterior) contacts and for annular eclipses. A smaller value (k=0.272281), representing a mean minimum radius, was reserved exclusively for umbral (i.e., interior) contact calculations of total eclipses (*Explanatory Supplement*, 1974). Unfortunately, the use of two different values of k for central eclipses introduces a discontinuity in the case of hybrid or annular-total eclipses.

In August 1982, the IAU General Assembly adopted a value of k=0.2725076 for the mean lunar radius. This value is currently used by the Nautical Almanac Office for all solar eclipse predictions (Fiala and Lukac, 1983) and is believed to be the best mean radius, averaging mountain peaks and low valleys along the Moon's rugged limb. The adoption of one single value for k eliminates the discontinuity in the case of annular-total eclipses and ends confusion arising from the use of two different values. However, the use of even the best 'mean' value for the Moon's radius introduces a problem in predicting the character and duration of central eclipses, particularly total eclipses. A total eclipse can be defined as an eclipse in which the Sun's disk is completely occulted by the Moon. This cannot occur so long as any photospheric rays are visible through deep valleys along the Moon's limb (Meeus, Grosjean and Vanderleen, 1966). But the use of the IAU's mean k guarantees that some annular or annular-total eclipses will be misidentified as total. For example, the *Astronomical Almanac for 1986* identified eclipse of 1986 Oct 03 as total with a 3 seconds duration when in it was in fact a beaded annular eclipse. Clearly, a smaller value of k is needed since it is more representative of the deepest lunar valley floors, hence the minimum solid disk radius, and ensures that an eclipse is truly total.

Of primary interest to most observers are the times when the central eclipse begins and ends (second and third contacts, respectively) and the duration of the central phase. When the IAU's mean value for k is used to calculate these times, they must be corrected to accommodate low valleys (total) or high mountains (annular) along the Moon's limb. The calculation of these corrections are essential, especially if one plans to observe near the path limits (Herald, 1983). For observers near the central line of a total eclipse, the limb corrections can be closely approximated by using a smaller value of k, which accounts for valleys along the profile.

This work uses the IAU's accepted value of k (k=0.2725076) for all penumbral (exterior) contacts. In order to avoid eclipse type misidentification and to predict central durations, which are closer to the actual durations observed at total eclipses, we depart from the IAU convention by adopting the smaller value for k (k=0.272281) for all central (interior) contacts. This is consistent with predictions published in Five Millennium Canon of Solar Eclipses (Espenak and Meeus, 2006) and *Thousand Year Canon of Solar Eclipses* (Espenak, 2014). Consequently, the smaller k produces shorter central durations and narrower paths for total eclipses when compared with calculations using the IAU value for k. Similarly, the smaller k predicts longer central durations and wider paths for annular eclipses.

1.8 Central Line and Duration of Totality

The axis of the Moon's shadow determines the central line of the path of totality (and annularity). For the purposes of this discussion, it is assumed that the central line lies in the middle of the eclipse path.[1]

The duration of totality is longest on the central line, so great effort is made to get as close as possible to it. However, the duration actually drops off quite slowly with distance from the central line. For example, a location 20% from the center to the edge of the path still has a totality lasting 95% of the central line duration. Even if one travels half way to the path limit, the duration is still 71% of the central line value.

---

[1] The position of the central line is actually offset from the center. The difference is greatest in cases where the Sun's altitude is low. Curvature of Earth's surface is responsible for this shift.

Figure 1–4: Duration Vs. Distance from the Central Line

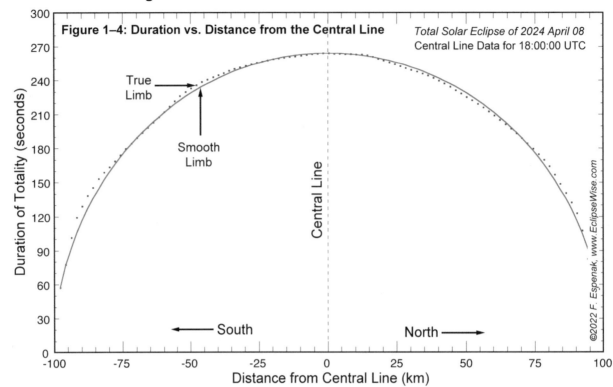

Figure 1–4 shows how the duration of totality changes with distance from the central line. The solid curve represents the duration using the Moon's mean limb. At a distance 67% from the central line to the path limit, the duration drops to 50%. It is only when the distance from the central line to the path limit reaches ~75% that the duration takes a precipitous drop. But even at a distance of 80%, the duration is still 31% of the central line value. The dotted curve uses the Moon's true limb to calculate the duration using data from NASA's Lunar Reconnaissance Orbiter.

Although figure 1–4 plots data for the 2024 total solar eclipse, the same relationship holds for all total eclipse paths. The solid curve is calculated assuming a smooth lunar limb. In reality, the Moon's limb profile has mountains that extend the duration and valleys that shorten it. These topographic features typically change the duration by a second or two for most of the path — their effects become significantly larger near the edges of the umbral path. The dotted line in figure 1–4 has been calculated using the Moon's true profile.

The following expression is useful for calculating the duration of totality for any location at a perpendicular distance of δ kilometers from the central line. It assumes a smooth profile for the Moon's limb.

$$d = D \times [\, 1 - (\, \delta/Z\,)^2\,]^{\frac{1}{2}} \text{ seconds} \qquad\qquad (1\text{–}2)$$

Where: d = duration of totality at point of interest (seconds)
D = duration of totality on the central line (seconds)
δ = perpendicular distance from the central line to position of interest (kilometers)
Z = perpendicular distance from the central line to the path edge (kilometers)

The Moon's limb profile varies with the lunar libration, which changes from eclipse to eclipse. Consequently, the effects of the limb profile are different at each eclipse.

1.9 Greatest Eclipse and Greatest Duration

Greatest Eclipse is defined as the instant when the axis of the Moon's shadow passes closest to the center of Earth. The computation of the duration of the total (or annular) phase at this point is typically done using a smooth Moon that ignores the effects of mountains and valleys along the lunar limb. For total eclipses, the instant of *Greatest Eclipse* offers a very good approximation (typically within 0.1 seconds) to the *Greatest Duration* of totality along the entire eclipse path.

Because of its rigorous geometric definition, the instant of *Greatest Eclipse* is easily calculated for total, annular and partial eclipses, and is the standard time used for comparing different eclipses with each other. For example, the time and date of each eclipse in the *Thousand Year Canon of Solar Eclipses: 1501 – 2500* (Espenak 2014) corresponds to the instant of *Greatest Eclipse*.

Greatest Duration is defined as the instant when the length of the total (or annular) phase reaches a maximum along the central eclipse path. The computation of the eclipse duration is again done using a smooth Moon that ignores the effects of mountains and valleys along the lunar limb. Although the location of *Greatest Duration* may be relatively close to the point of *Greatest Eclipse*, it differs slightly because of several factors including Earth's oblateness, the relative motion of the Moon's shadow with respect to Earth's Equator, and the latitude of the shadow axis.

The length of the total eclipse calculated at *Greatest Duration* is typically 0.1 seconds longer compared with *Greatest Eclipse*, and the geographic location typically differs by about 75 kilometers. These values are based on the 67 central total solar eclipses occurring during the 21st Century. The statistics for *Greatest Eclipse (GE)* vs. *Greatest Duration (GD)* for these eclipses are as follows.

Greatest Eclipse and Greatest Duration for
Total Solar Eclipses of the 21st Century

Statistic	Duration (GD–GE)	Distance (GD-GE)
Average	0.084 sec	74.2 km
Std. Dev.	0.138 sec	66.2 km
Minimum	0.000 sec	2.5 km
Maximum	0.608 sec	251.6 km

Unlike *Greatest Eclipse*, there is no explicit or analytical solution for the determination of *Greatest Duration*. It may be calculated though an iterative series of approximations. When the highest accuracy is needed, a *Corrected Greatest Duration* must be calculated that includes the effects of the Moon's limb profile, which may differ by a couple seconds from the uncorrected value. (see next section)

The table below summarizes the values for *Greatest Eclipse* and *Greatest Duration* for the total solar eclipse of 2024 April 08. The central line duration of totality is 0.053 seconds longer at the point of *Greatest Duration*, which lies 95.4 km northeast of the point of *Greatest Eclipse*.

Greatest Eclipse and Greatest Duration for 2024 April 08

Event	Time (UTC)	Latitude	Longitude	Duration
Greatest Eclipse:	18:17:20.2	25°17.4'N	104°08.9'W	04m28.13s
Greatest Duration:	18:19:36.2	25°56.1'N	103°31.3'W	04m28.19s

1.10 Lunar Limb Profile

Eclipse contact times, magnitude, and duration of totality all depend on the angular diameters and relative velocities of the Moon and Sun. Unfortunately, these calculations are limited in accuracy by the departure of the Moon's limb from a perfectly circular figure. The Moon's surface exhibits a dramatic topography, which manifests itself as an irregular limb when seen in profile. Most eclipse calculations assume a mean radius that averages high mountain peaks and low valleys along the Moon's limb. Such an approximation is acceptable for many applications, but when higher accuracy is needed the Moon's actual limb profile must be considered.

For many years, Watts's limb charts (Watts 1963) constituted the most detailed maps of lunar mountain profiles at all libration phases. These data were the product of a photographic survey of the marginal zone of the Moon and give limb profile heights with respect to an adopted smooth reference surface (or datum).

Figure 1–5: Lunar Limb Profile for 2024 April 08 at 18:15 UTC

Maximum Eclipse = 18:15:00.0 UTC

Magnitude = 1.0566   Ratio = 1.0566

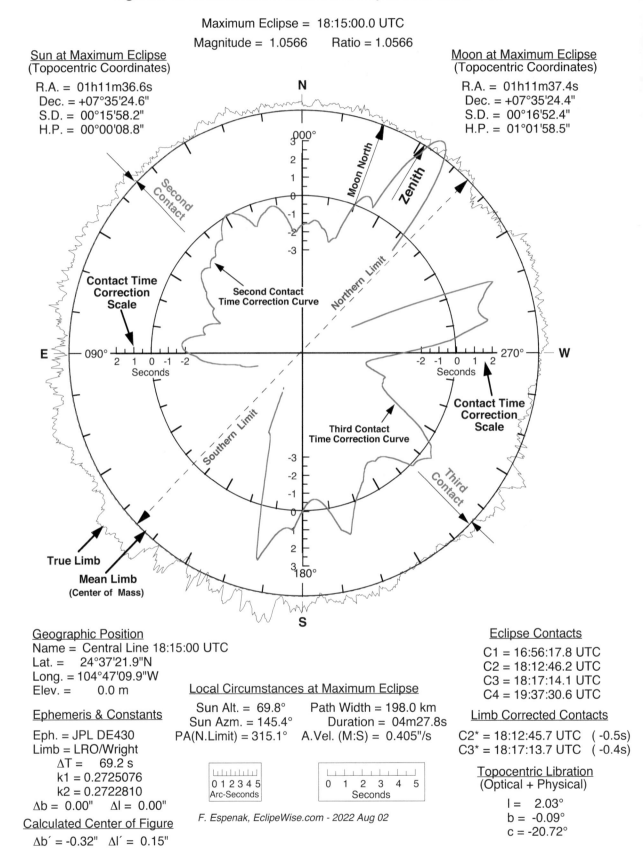

Sun at Maximum Eclipse
(Topocentric Coordinates)

R.A. = 01h11m36.6s
Dec. = +07°35'24.6"
S.D. = 00°15'58.2"
H.P. = 00°00'08.8"

Moon at Maximum Eclipse
(Topocentric Coordinates)

R.A. = 01h11m37.4s
Dec. = +07°35'24.4"
S.D. = 00°16'52.4"
H.P. = 01°01'58.5"

Geographic Position
Name = Central Line 18:15:00 UTC
Lat. =   24°37'21.9"N
Long. = 104°47'09.9"W
Elev. =   0.0 m

Ephemeris & Constants

Eph. = JPL DE430
Limb = LRO/Wright
    ΔT =   69.2 s
    k1 = 0.2725076
    k2 = 0.2722810
Δb = 0.00" Δl = 0.00"

Calculated Center of Figure
    $\Delta b'$ = -0.32" $\Delta l'$ = 0.15"

Local Circumstances at Maximum Eclipse

Sun Alt. = 69.8°   Path Width = 198.0 km
Sun Azm. = 145.4°   Duration = 04m27.8s
PA(N.Limit) = 315.1°   A.Vel. (M:S) = 0.405"/s

F. Espenak, EclipeWise.com - 2022 Aug 02

Eclipse Contacts

C1 = 16:56:17.8 UTC
C2 = 18:12:46.2 UTC
C3 = 18:17:14.1 UTC
C4 = 19:37:30.6 UTC

Limb Corrected Contacts

C2* = 18:12:45.7 UTC (-0.5s)
C3* = 18:17:13.7 UTC (-0.4s)

Topocentric Libration
(Optical + Physical)

l =   2.03°
b = -0.09°
c = -20.72°

In 2015, E. Wright (NASA/GSFC) used measurements from the Lunar Orbiter Laser Altimeter (LOLA) aboard NASA's Lunar Reconnaissance Orbiter (LRO) to develop a altitude/libration dataset and converted it into a Watts-like format including the difference between the center of mass and center of figure. It provides the angular height of the actual lunar limb above a mean lunar limb (k=0.2725076 in Earth radii of 6378.137 km) as a function of position angle (0.05° increments) and libration (0.05° increments in L and B) relative to the Moon's center of mass, with the Moon at its mean distance (384398.55 km).

Along the entire 2024 total eclipse path, the Moon's topocentric libration (physical plus optical) in longitude ranges from l = +2.79° to +1.22° (l = +2.11° to +1.26° across the section of the path through North America). Thus, a limb profile with the appropriate libration is required in any detailed analysis of contact times, central durations, etc. However, a profile with an intermediate value is useful for planning purposes and may even be adequate for many applications.

The lunar limb profile in Figure 1–5 is derived from the LRO dataset with respect to the Moon's center of mass. It is generated for 18:15 UTC (within three minutes of the instant of greatest eclipse). The umbral shadow is then located in northern Mexico at latitude 24° 37.4'N and longitude 104° 47.2'W. The Moon's topocentric libration is l = +2.03°, b = −0.09° and the topocentric semi-diameters of the Sun and Moon are 958.2 and 1012.4 arc-seconds, respectively. The Moon's angular velocity with respect to the Sun is 0.405 arc-seconds/second.

Lunar limb profiles for three additional positions along the central line (for 18:45 UTC, 19:15 UTC, and 19:45 UTC) are available at: www.eclipsewise.com/news/2024.html

The radial scale of the limb profile in Figure 1–5 is greatly exaggerated so that the true limb's departure from the mean limb is readily apparent. Note that some predictions presented in this publication are calculated with respect to the mean limb unless otherwise noted. Position angles of various lunar features can be read using the protractor marks along the Moon's mean limb. The position angles of second and third contact are clearly marked, as are the north pole of the Moon's axis of rotation and the observer's zenith at mid-totality. The dashed line with arrows at either end identifies the contact points on the limb corresponding to the northern and southern limits of the path. To the upper left of the profile, are the Sun's topocentric coordinates at maximum eclipse. They include the right ascension *(R.A.)*, declination *(Dec.)*, semi-diameter *(S.D.)*, and horizontal parallax *(H.P.)*. The corresponding topocentric coordinates for the Moon appear to the upper right. Below and left of the profile are the geographic coordinates of the central line at selected location, while the times of the four eclipse contacts at that location appear to the lower right. The limb-corrected times of second and third contacts are listed with the applied correction to the center of mass smooth limb prediction.

Directly below the limb profile are the local circumstances at maximum eclipse. They include the Sun's altitude and azimuth, the path width, and duration. The position angle of the path's northern-to-southern limit axis is *PA (N.Limit)* and the angular velocity of the Moon with respect to the Sun is *A.Vel. (M:S)*. At the bottom left are a number of parameters used in the predictions, and the topocentric lunar librations appear at the lower right.

As mentioned earlier, the four eclipse contact times for the central line position at 18:15 UTC are listed to the lower right of the limb profile (Figure 1–5). These are calculated using a smooth limb. When the LRO limb profile is applied to C2 and C3 (start and end of totality), the resulting values appear under *Limb Corrected Contacts*. The numbers in the brackets, (−0.5s) and (−0.4s), are the corrections added to smooth limb C2 and C3 times to compensate for the actual lunar limb profile. In this case, the duration of totality is 0.1 seconds longer (4 min 27.9 sec) than the smooth limb duration (4 min 27.8 sec).

The extended duration of totality at this central line position is not unique. The large, mountainous terrain in the eastern quadrant of the lunar limb profile in Figure 1–5 is partly responsible for extending the smooth limb durations (up to 0.7 seconds) along some sections of the eclipse track across North America (Table 1–9).

Table 1–9 consists, in part, of data extracted from Tables 1–3 and 1–6. It lists the central line time of mid-eclipse and longitude of the umbral path across North America, the Moon's topocentric libration in longitude and the central line duration calculated using a smooth lunar limb. The computed limb correction due to the LRO profile, and the resulting central line duration are given next (the last two columns will be discussed shortly). Of interest is the data for the 18:20 UTC central line position. It shows the longest duration of totality along the entire path of 4 minutes 28.2 seconds. In this instance, the lunar limb profile has no effect on the duration of totality on the central line.

Table 1–9: Correction to Central Line Duration of Totality Due To Lunar Limb Profile

UTC	Central Line Longitude	Topo. Lib. Long.	Central Line Duration (smooth)	Lunar Limb Correction (seconds)	Central Line Duration (corrected)	Maximum Duration Correction (seconds)	Maximum Duration (corrected)	Maximum Duration Shift (km)
18:10	106°07.9'W	2.07	04m27.2s	-0.07	04m27.2s	0.21	04m27.4s	-2.0
18:15	104°47.2'W	2.03	04m28.0s	-0.07	04m27.9s	0.24	04m28.1s	-2.3
18:20	103°24.7'W	1.99	04m28.2s	-0.03	04m28.2s	0.25	04m28.4s	-2.4
18:25	101°59.8'W	1.94	04m27.9s	0.02	04m27.9s	0.28	04m28.2s	-2.7
18:30	100°31.8'W	1.90	04m27.0s	0.08	04m27.1s	0.31	04m27.4s	-3.1
18:35	099°00.0'W	1.86	04m25.6s	0.14	04m25.8s	0.24	04m26.0s	-2.3
18:40	097°23.4'W	1.82	04m23.7s	0.27	04m24.0s	0.14	04m24.1s	-1.4
18:45	095°41.1'W	1.77	04m21.2s	0.46	04m21.6s	0.03	04m21.7s	-0.3
18:50	093°52.0'W	1.73	04m18.1s	0.47	04m18.5s	0.08	04m18.6s	0.7
18:55	091°54.8'W	1.69	04m14.4s	0.58	04m14.9s	0.17	04m15.1s	1.5
19:00	089°48.0'W	1.64	04m10.0s	0.66	04m10.7s	0.32	04m11.0s	2.8
19:05	087°29.8'W	1.60	04m05.1s	0.68	04m05.7s	0.12	04m05.9s	1.1
19:10	084°57.9'W	1.56	03m59.4s	0.67	04m00.1s	0.05	04m00.1s	-0.5
19:15	082°09.5'W	1.52	03m53.1s	0.56	03m53.6s	0.24	03m53.9s	-2.1
19:20	079°01.0'W	1.47	03m46.0s	0.61	03m46.6s	0.29	03m46.9s	-3.7
19:25	075°27.4'W	1.43	03m38.0s	0.36	03m38.4s	0.53	03m38.9s	-5.3
19:30	071°21.8'W	1.39	03m29.1s	-0.01	03m29.1s	1.01	03m30.1s	-7.2
19:35	066°34.1'W	1.35	03m19.2s	-0.35	03m18.8s	1.48	03m20.3s	-9.1
19:40	060°47.5'W	1.31	03m07.8s	-0.57	03m07.2s	1.87	03m09.1s	-9.0
19:45	053°29.8'W	1.26	02m54.4s	-0.81	02m53.6s	1.79	02m55.4s	-8.7

1.11 Limb Profile Effects on the Maximum Duration of Totality

In the previously section, we discussed how the irregularities in the Moon's limb profile affect the duration of totality on the central line. For some eclipses, deep valleys along the limb can shorten the length of totality. But in the case of the 2024 eclipse, the duration is lengthened as much as 0.7 seconds because of a mountainous region in the eastern quadrant of the Moon.

Figure 1–6 shows a series of calculations for the duration of totality within ±60 kilometers of the central line for six locations spaced at 10-minute intervals along the path through North America. For a given time, the duration of totality is calculated at 0.1 kilometer intervals perpendicular to the path within a 200 kilometer zone centered on the central line. Predictions using the Moon's center of mass and mean (smooth) limb are represented by the solid curves. Predictions using the LRO limb profile to calculate corrected contact times and the resulting durations of totality are plotted as dotted curves.

What is immediately apparent in Figure 1–6, is the skewing of the limb-corrected duration curves. This is a consequence of the complex Sun/Moon limb geometry, which changes significantly with the observer's position along the path. While the mean limb duration curves (solid) appear symmetric about the central line, the limb-corrected duration curves are decidedly asymmetric and peak several kilometers to the south of the central line (especially for 19:15 UTC and later). Furthermore, the durations at these shifted positions actually exceed the durations on the central line. In other words, when the lunar limb profile is taken into account, the maximum duration does *NOT* occur on the central line as conventional wisdom would suggest, but rather at several kilometers to the south of the central line (at least, in the case of the 2024 total eclipse).

The shifts south of the central line to maximize the duration, as well as the corresponding duration values appear in the last two columns of Table 1–9. The shifts to maximum duration beginning 19:15 UTC range from 2.1 to 9.1 km south of the central line with gains in duration from 0.2 to 1.9 seconds. This section of the path from 19:15 UTC and after corresponds to Ohio through Newfoundland. Observers wishing to witness the maximum possible duration of totality from a given section of the path can use Table 1–9 to optimize their location with respect to the central line.

Figure 1–6: Limb Profile Effects on the Duration of Totality

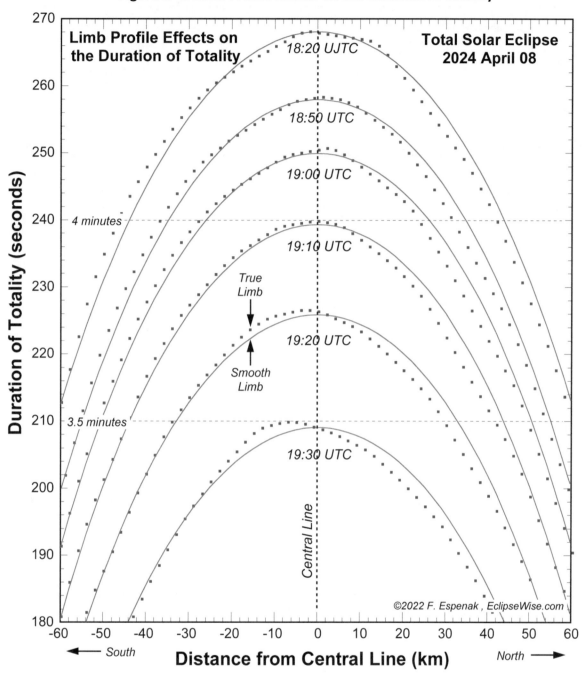

Figure 1–7 illustrates this information with two graphs covering longitudes from 120°W to 40°W. The top graph shows the difference in seconds between the point of maximum duration and the central line. The point of maximum duration is found along a line perpendicular to the central line by calculating the duration every 0.1 km across the path and includes the effects of the lunar limb profile. Of particular note in this figure is the pronounced increase in the difference between maximum duration and the central line duration.

The lower graph shows how far the point of maximum duration lies from the central line in kilometers. The maximum shift runs from New Brunswick to Newfoundland where maximum duration is up to 9 km south of the central line and the duration is 1.0 to 1.9 seconds longer than the central line duration.

Figure 1–7: Duration on the Central Line and the Point of Maximum Duration

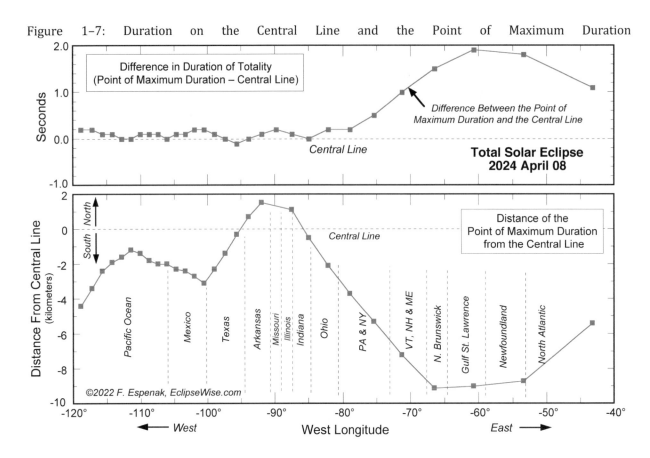

1.12 Limb Corrections to the Path Limits: Graze Zones

The northern and southern umbral limits provided in this publication were derived using the Moon's center of mass and a mean lunar radius. They have not been corrected for the effects of the lunar limb profile. In applications where precise limits are required, the LRO limb data must be used to correct the nominal or mean path. Unfortunately, a single correction at each limit is not possible because the Moon's libration in longitude and the contact points of the limits along the Moon's limb each vary as a function of time and position along the umbral path. This makes it necessary to calculate a unique correction to the limits at each point along the path. Furthermore, the northern and southern limits of the umbral path are actually paralleled by a relatively narrow zone where the eclipse is neither partial nor total. An observer positioned here will witness a slender solar crescent that is fragmented into a series of bright beads and short segments whose morphology changes quickly with the rapidly varying geometry between the limbs of the Moon and the Sun. These beading phenomena are caused by the appearance of photospheric rays that alternately pass through deep lunar valleys and hide behind high mountain peaks, as the Moon's irregular limb grazes the edge of the Sun's disk. The geometry is directly analogous to the case of grazing occultations of stars by the Moon. The graze zone is typically 5–10 km wide and its interior and exterior boundaries can be predicted using the lunar limb profile. The interior boundaries define the actual limits of the umbral eclipse (both total and annular) while the exterior boundaries set the outer limits of the grazing eclipse zone.

Table 1–6 provides topocentric data and corrections to the path limits due to the true lunar limb profile. At 5-minute intervals, the table lists the Moon's topocentric horizontal parallax, semi-diameter, relative angular velocity with respect to the Sun, and lunar libration in longitude. The Sun's central line altitude and azimuth is given, followed by the azimuth of the umbral path. The position angle of the point on the Moon's limb, which defines the northern limit of the path, is measured counterclockwise (i.e., eastward) from the equatorial north point on the limb. The path corrections to the northern and southern limits are listed as interior and exterior components in order to define the graze zone. Positive corrections are in the northern sense, while negative shifts are in the southern sense. These corrections (minutes of arc in latitude) may be added directly to the path coordinates listed in Table 1–3. Corrections to the central line umbral durations due to the lunar limb profile are also included and they are mostly positive; thus, when added to the central durations given in Tables 1–3, 1–4, 1–5, and 1–7, a slightly longer central total phase is predicted. This effect is due to a mountainous region in the eastern quadrant of the Moon for the predicted librations during the 2024 eclipse.

Detailed coordinates for the zones of grazing eclipse at each limit along the path are presented in Table 1–8a (online at *www.eclipsewise.com/news/2024.html*). Given the uncertainties in the limb data, these predictions should be accurate to ±0.3 arc-seconds. (The interior graze coordinates take into account the deepest valleys along the Moon's limb, which produce the simultaneous second and third contacts at the path limits; thus, the interior coordinates that define the true edge of the path of totality.) They are calculated from an algorithm that searches the path limits for the extreme positions where no photospheric beads are visible along a ±30° segment of the Moon's limb, symmetric about the extreme contact points at the instant of maximum eclipse. The exterior graze coordinates are arbitrarily defined and calculated for the geodetic positions where an unbroken photospheric crescent of 60° in angular extent is visible at maximum eclipse.

In Table 1–8a, the graze zone latitudes are listed every 0.5° in longitude (at sea level) and include the time of maximum eclipse at the northern and southern limits, as well as the path's azimuth. To correct the path for locations above sea level, *Elev Fact* (elevation factor) is a multiplicative factor by which the path must be shifted north or south perpendicular to itself, i.e., perpendicular to path azimuth, for each unit of elevation (height) above sea level.

The elevation factor is the product, $\tan(90-A) \times \sin(D)$, where A is the altitude of the Sun, and D is the difference between the azimuth of the Sun and the azimuth of the limit line, with the sign selected to be positive if the path should be shifted north with elevations above sea level. To calculate the shift, a location's elevation is multiplied by the elevation factor value. Negative values (usually the case for eclipses in the Northern Hemisphere) indicate that the path must be shifted south. For instance, if one's elevation is 1000 m above sea level and the elevation factor value is –0.50, then the shift is –500 m (= 1000 m × –0.50); thus, the observer must shift the path coordinates 500 m in a direction perpendicular to the path and in a negative or southerly sense.

The final column of Table 1–8a lists the *Scale Fact* (in kilometers per arc second). This parameter provides an indication of the width of the zone of grazing phenomena, due to the topocentric distance of the Moon and the projection geometry of the Moon's shadow on Earth's surface. Because the solar chromosphere has an apparent thickness of about 3 arc-seconds, and assuming a scaling factor value of 1.75 km/arc-second, then the chromosphere should be visible continuously during totality for any observer in the path who is within 5.2 km (=1.75 × 3) of each interior limit. The most dynamic beading phenomena, however, occurs within 1.5 arc-seconds of the Moon's limb. Using the above scaling factor, this translates to the first 2.6 km inside the interior limits, but observers should position themselves at least 1 km inside the interior limits (south of the northern interior limit or north of the southern interior limit) in order to ensure that they are inside the path because of small uncertainties in the LRO data and the actual path limits.

For applications where the zones of grazing eclipse are needed at a higher frequency of longitude interval, Table 1–8b (*www.eclipsewise.com/news/2024.html*) gives coordinates every 7.5′ in longitude.

Photo 1–4: Baily's beads appear at 3rd contact as sunlight shines through deep valleys along the Moon's limb, This image sequence was shot at the total solar eclipse of 2006 Mar 29 from Jalu, Libya. © 2006 by F. Espenak, www.MrEclipse.com

Section 2: Local Circumstances for the Eclipse

2.1 Introduction

As the Moon's umbral and penumbral shadows sweep across Earth's surface, different geographic locations are in different parts of either of the two shadows at any given time. The penumbral shadow is quite large and has a diameter of about 6800 km (4200 mi) during the 2024 eclipse. Because of this, the entire North American continent (except Alaska) and much of the Pacific Ocean fall within its path, and a partial solar eclipse will be visible from the region.

In contrast, the umbral shadow is quite narrow and an observer must be somewhere within its path in order to see the total phase of the eclipse. The width of the umbral path ranges from 142 to 199 kilometers (88 to 123 miles) during the 2024 eclipse.

Figure 2–1: Moon's Shadows and Local Circumstances

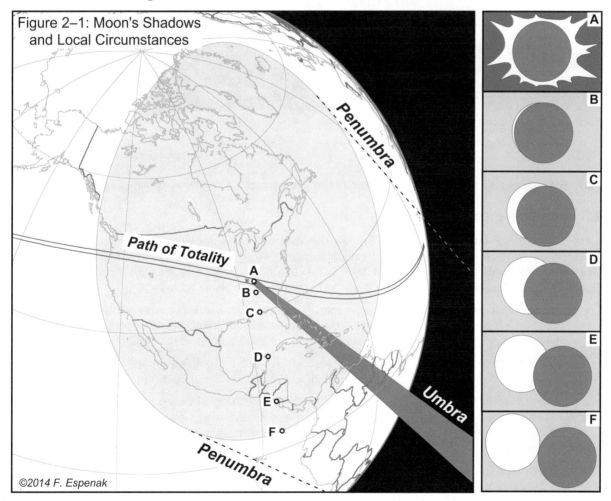

Figure 2–1 illustrates the path of totality for a typical total solar eclipse (2017 August 21). The appearance of maximum eclipse from six different geographic locations on the map (labeled A through F) is shown in the side bar. The total eclipse is visible only from position A because it lies in the path of totality.

Figure 2–1 demonstrates how observers at different locations can observe different phases of the eclipse (or even no eclipse) at the same instant. Because of this, the beginning, middle and end times of the eclipse, its magnitude at maximum, and the Sun's altitude and azimuth at each phase of the eclipse (i.e., the local circumstances of the eclipse), will be different for any two locations.

2.2 Solar Eclipse Contacts

During the course of a solar eclipse, the instants when the Moon's disk becomes tangent to the Sun's disk are known as eclipse contacts. They mark various stages or phases of a solar eclipse.

Partial solar eclipses have two primary contacts.

First Contact (C1) —   Instant of first exterior tangency of the Moon with the Sun (Partial Eclipse Begins)
Fourth Contact (C4) — Instant of last exterior tangency of the Moon with the Sun (Partial Eclipse Ends)

Total solar eclipses have four primary contacts. Contacts C2 and C3 mark the instants when the Moon's disk is first and last internally tangent to the Sun. These are the times when the annular or total phase of the eclipse begins and ends, respectively.

First Contact (C1) —   Instant of first exterior tangency of the Moon with the Sun (Partial Eclipse Begins)
Second Contact (C2) —   Instant of first interior tangency of the Moon with the Sun (Total Eclipse Begins)
Third Contact (C3) —   Instant of last interior tangency of the Moon with the Sun (Total Eclipse Ends)
Fourth Contact (C4) —   Instant of last exterior tangency of the Moon with the Sun (Partial Eclipse Ends)

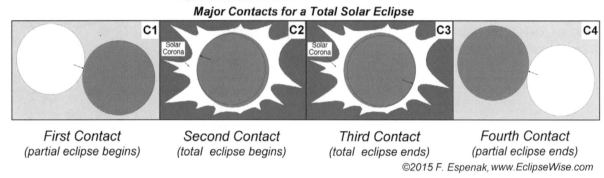

Major Contacts for a Total Solar Eclipse

First Contact	Second Contact	Third Contact	Fourth Contact
(partial eclipse begins)	*(total eclipse begins)*	*(total eclipse ends)*	*(partial eclipse ends)*

©2015 F. Espenak, www.EclipseWise.com

Figure 2–1 The four contacts for a total solar eclipse. The arrows indicate the contact point of the Sun's limb in each diagram.

2.3 Local Circumstances Tables

Local circumstances for the 2024 eclipse as seen from over 600 cities throughout the United States are found in Tables 2–1 through 2–8. The eclipse circumstances for ~80 cities in Mexico appear in Table 2–9, and for ~115 cities in Canada in Tables 2–10 and 2–11. Local circumstances for other regions include North Atlantic (Table 2-12), Central and South America (Table 2-13), and the Caribbean (Table 2–14).

The tables give the local circumstances at each contact and at maximum eclipse for every location. For locations where the eclipse is partial, maximum eclipse is the instant when the greatest fraction of the Sun's diameter is occulted. For locations where the eclipse is total, maximum eclipse is the instant of mid-totality.

For cities in the path of totality, the times of second and third contacts (the start and end of totality, respectively), include corrections for the Moon's limb profile as described in Section 1.10.

The times are in *local time* for each city. The eclipse occurs when *Daylight Saving Time* or *DST* is in effect in many states and provinces (exceptions include Arizona, Hawaii, and Saskatchewan). Where applicable, *DST* has been included in calculating the local time (Mexican municipalities along the US border use *DST* while the rest of Mexico does not).

The times of first and fourth contacts (beginning and ending of partial eclipse) are given to 1 second, while second and third contacts (beginning and ending of totality) are given to a precision of 0.1 second. The position angle **V** and the altitude of the Sun are also given at each contact. The position angle identifies the point along the Sun's disk where each contact occurs and is measured counterclockwise (i.e., eastward) from the zenith point or top of Sun's disk. Locations outside the umbral path miss the total eclipse and only witness first and fourth contacts. The time of maximum eclipse (either partial or total) is also listed to the nearest second. Next, the position angle **V** of the Moon's disk with respect to the Sun is given followed by the altitude and azimuth of the Sun at maximum eclipse. Finally, the corresponding eclipse magnitude[1] and obscuration[2] are listed. For total eclipses, the eclipse magnitude given is actually the topocentric ratio of the Moon and Sun's apparent diameters, rather than the fraction of the Sun's diameter occulted.

Two additional columns are included if the location lies within the path of the Moon's umbral shadow. The *FDCL* (Fractional Distance to the Central Line) is a relative measure of a location's position with respect to the central line and umbral path limits. It is a unitless parameter, which is defined as

$$FDCL = 2\ x/W, \tag{2-1}$$

where:

FDCL is the Fractional Distance to the Central Line,
x is the perpendicular distance from the central line in kilometers, and
W is the width of the path in kilometers.

The *FDCL* for a location in the path of totality varies from 0.0 to 1.0. A position on the central line corresponds to a value of 0.0 while a position on the path limits corresponds to a value of 1.0. The sign of DFCL indicates whether a location is north (+) or south (−) of the central line. The parameter can be used to quickly determine the corresponding central line duration. Thus, it is a useful tool for evaluating the trade-off in duration of a location's position relative to the central line. Using the location's duration and Umbral Depth, the central line duration is calculated as

$$D = d\ /\ [1 - FDCL^2]^{1/2}, \tag{2-2}$$

where:

D is the duration of totality on the central line (seconds),
d is the duration of totality at location (seconds), and
FDCL is the Fractional Distance to the Central Line.

The final column *Durat. Total.* gives the duration of totality. This value includes the effects of the lunar limb profile (see Section 1.10).

Locations were chosen based on general geographic distribution, population, and proximity to the path. The primary source for geographic coordinates is *The New International Atlas* (Rand McNally 1991) with updates for the changing political landscape. In this rapidly changing world, it is often difficult to ascertain the correct name or spelling for a given location; therefore, the information presented here is for location purposes only and is not meant to be authoritative. Corrections to names, spellings, and coordinates, should be forwarded to the authors at *www.eclipsewise.com/main/contact.html*.

---

1 Eclipse magnitude is defined as the fraction of the Sun's *diameter* occulted by the Moon.

2 Eclipse obscuration is defined as the fraction of the Sun's *area* occulted by the Moon.

Table 2–1: Local Circumstances for Alabama – California

Location	Lat °	Long °	First Contact Time h m s	First Contact V °	First Contact Alt °	Second Contact Time h m s	Second Contact V °	Third Contact Time h m s	Third Contact V °	Fourth Contact Time h m s	Fourth Contact V °	Fourth Contact Alt °	Middle Eclipse Time h m s	Middle Eclipse V °	Middle Eclipse Alt °	Middle Eclipse Azm °	Ecl. Mag.	Ecl. Obs.	FDCL	Durat Total
Alabama																				
Anniston	33.65	-85.83	12:42:55	238	64	–	–	–	–	15:19:09	354	46	14:02:05	288	58	219	0.867	0.844		
Auburn	32.60	-85.48	12:42:15	240	65	–	–	–	–	15:18:25	350	46	14:01:24	286	59	220	0.833	0.801		
Birmingham	33.52	-86.80	12:40:58	240	64	–	–	–	–	15:17:48	355	47	14:00:19	289	59	217	0.879	0.860		
Decatur	34.60	-86.98	12:42:07	238	63	–	–	–	–	15:18:39	358	46	14:01:19	290	58	216	0.911	0.900		
Dothan	31.22	-85.40	12:40:41	242	66	–	–	–	–	15:16:47	346	47	13:59:46	284	60	221	0.794	0.752		
Gadsden	34.02	-86.02	12:43:04	238	64	–	–	–	–	15:19:19	355	46	14:02:14	288	58	218	0.880	0.860		
Hoover	33.40	-86.80	12:40:48	240	64	–	–	–	–	15:17:40	355	47	14:00:10	289	59	217	0.876	0.856		
Huntsville	34.73	-86.58	12:43:00	237	63	–	–	–	–	15:19:18	358	46	14:02:09	290	58	216	0.908	0.896		
Mobile	30.68	-88.05	12:34:42	249	66	–	–	–	–	15:12:45	349	50	13:54:23	288	63	215	0.827	0.793		
Montgomery	32.38	-86.32	12:40:21	242	65	–	–	–	–	15:17:08	351	47	13:59:42	287	60	218	0.841	0.811		
Tuscaloosa	33.20	-87.57	12:39:07	242	64	–	–	–	–	15:16:28	355	48	13:58:37	290	60	215	0.884	0.866		
Arizona																				
Chandler	33.30	-111.83	10:08:13	257	49	–	–	–	–	12:35:23	62	64	11:20:07	167	60	144	0.712	0.649		
Flagstaff	35.20	-111.65	10:12:48	252	48	–	–	–	–	12:37:37	63	62	11:23:42	164	59	148	0.680	0.609		
Gilbert	33.35	-111.78	10:08:22	257	49	–	–	–	–	12:35:33	62	64	11:20:17	167	60	145	0.712	0.649		
Glendale	33.53	-112.18	10:08:30	256	48	–	–	–	–	12:34:53	63	64	11:20:01	167	59	144	0.701	0.636		
Mesa	33.42	-111.83	10:08:29	257	49	–	–	–	–	12:35:30	62	64	11:20:19	167	60	145	0.710	0.647		
Nogales	31.33	-110.93	10:04:23	262	49	–	–	–	–	12:35:08	56	66	11:17:57	168	62	143	0.767	0.717		
Peoria	33.58	-112.23	10:08:35	256	48	–	–	–	–	12:34:50	64	64	11:20:02	167	59	144	0.700	0.633		
Phoenix	33.45	-112.07	10:08:24	257	48	–	–	–	–	12:35:03	63	64	11:20:03	167	60	144	0.705	0.640		
Scottsdale	33.48	-111.93	10:08:34	257	48	–	–	–	–	12:35:22	62	64	11:20:17	167	60	144	0.707	0.643		
Tempe	33.42	-111.93	10:08:25	257	48	–	–	–	–	12:35:18	62	64	11:20:10	167	60	144	0.708	0.644		
Tucson	32.22	-110.97	10:06:23	260	49	–	–	–	–	12:36:04	57	65	11:19:29	167	61	145	0.749	0.695		
Yuma	32.72	-114.62	10:04:57	258	46	–	–	–	–	12:28:51	73	65	11:15:02	173	58	137	0.670	0.597		
Arkansas																				
Arkadelphia	34.12	-93.07	12:31:17	248	62	13:49:35.5	93	13:51:45.9	150	15:09:49	7	52	13:50:44	302	62	200	1.055	1.000	-0.878	02m04s
Benton	34.57	-92.58	12:32:47	246	62	13:50:46.2	84	13:53:26.5	158	15:10:58	7	52	13:52:08	301	62	201	1.055	1.000	-0.793	02m37s
Cabot	34.98	-92.02	12:34:21	244	61	13:52:13.8	82	13:54:56.4	158	15:12:10	7	51	13:53:37	300	61	203	1.055	1.000	-0.783	02m39s
Conway	35.08	-92.43	12:33:53	245	61	13:51:05.9	57	13:54:59.5	184	15:11:40	8	51	13:53:04	301	61	202	1.055	1.000	-0.430	03m51s
Fayetteville	36.07	-94.17	12:33:02	244	60	–	–	–	–	15:09:55	14	52	13:51:37	125	61	197	0.985	0.989		
Florence	33.77	-91.65	12:32:56	247	63	–	–	–	–	15:11:31	3	51	13:52:34	298	62	204	0.969	0.972		
Fort Smith	35.42	-94.42	12:31:32	246	60	–	–	–	–	15:09:00	13	53	13:50:21	125	61	196	0.996	0.998		
Harrison	36.23	-93.12	12:34:50	243	60	–	–	–	–	15:11:37	13	51	13:53:29	123	60	200	0.999	0.999		
Hot Springs	34.50	-93.05	12:31:57	247	61	13:49:28.7	66	13:53:05.6	177	15:10:13	8	52	13:51:17	302	62	200	1.055	1.000	-0.552	03m35s
Jacksonville	34.87	-92.12	12:34:01	245	61	13:52:00.7	86	13:54:30.5	154	15:11:55	7	51	13:53:18	300	61	203	1.055	1.000	-0.824	02m25s
Jonesboro	35.83	-90.70	12:37:47	241	61	13:55:34.5	85	13:57:58.8	151	15:14:46	7	49	13:56:49	298	59	206	1.055	1.000	-0.835	02m19s
Little Rock	34.75	-92.28	12:33:33	245	62	13:51:34.7	86	13:54:05.7	154	15:11:35	7	51	13:52:52	300	61	202	1.055	1.000	-0.821	02m27s
Mountain Home	36.33	-92.38	12:36:04	242	60	13:53:09.8	351	13:56:20.8	252	15:12:46	12	50	13:54:46	121	60	202	1.055	1.000	0.657	03m11s
North Little Roc	34.75	-92.27	12:33:35	245	62	13:51:38.1	87	13:54:05.2	153	15:11:36	7	51	13:52:54	300	61	202	1.055	1.000	-0.833	02m22s
Paragould	36.05	-90.48	12:38:28	240	61	13:56:02.0	78	13:58:46.2	157	15:15:15	8	49	13:57:25	298	59	207	1.055	1.000	-0.769	02m42s
Pine Bluff	34.22	-92.02	12:33:05	246	62	–	–	–	–	15:11:27	5	51	13:52:35	299	62	203	0.987	0.991		
Russellville	35.28	-93.13	12:33:10	245	61	13:50:06.2	22	13:54:16.7	222	15:10:49	10	52	13:52:13	122	61	200	1.055	1.000	0.193	04m11s
Searcy	35.25	-91.73	12:35:14	243	61	13:52:55.5	76	13:55:52.5	162	15:12:49	8	50	13:54:25	299	60	204	1.055	1.000	-0.722	02m57s
Sherwood	34.82	-92.22	12:33:46	245	61	13:51:43.8	84	13:54:20.1	156	15:11:44	7	51	13:53:04	300	61	202	1.055	1.000	-0.805	02m32s
Texarkana	33.43	-94.05	12:28:35	251	62	13:46:51.3	90	13:49:22.2	157	15:07:40	7	54	13:48:09	304	63	197	1.056	1.000	-0.827	02m26s
California																				
Anaheim	33.83	-117.92	10:05:48	254	43	–	–	–	–	12:22:42	87	63	11:12:24	176	55	133	0.589	0.500		
Bakersfield	35.38	-119.02	10:09:08	250	43	–	–	–	–	12:21:39	91	61	11:13:40	175	53	133	0.544	0.447		
Calexico	32.67	-115.50	10:04:17	258	45	–	–	–	–	12:26:53	77	65	11:13:41	174	57	135	0.654	0.578		
Chula Vista	32.65	-117.08	10:03:21	257	44	–	–	–	–	12:23:22	83	64	11:11:25	177	56	132	0.625	0.542		
Cucamonga	34.10	-117.60	10:06:37	253	44	–	–	–	–	12:23:40	86	63	11:13:19	175	55	134	0.591	0.501		
Escondido	33.12	-117.08	10:04:29	256	44	–	–	–	–	12:23:51	83	64	11:12:16	176	56	133	0.617	0.533		
Fairfield	38.25	-122.05	10:15:20	241	40	–	–	–	–	12:17:02	103	57	11:14:42	175	50	132	0.447	0.339		
Fremont	37.53	-121.95	10:13:32	243	40	–	–	–	–	12:16:43	102	58	11:13:35	176	50	131	0.460	0.352		
Fresno	36.70	-119.78	10:12:07	246	42	–	–	–	–	12:21:02	94	60	11:14:58	175	52	134	0.509	0.407		
Fullerton	33.88	-117.93	10:05:55	254	43	–	–	–	–	12:22:42	87	63	11:12:28	176	55	133	0.588	0.499		
Garden Grove	33.78	-117.92	10:05:41	254	43	–	–	–	–	12:22:39	87	63	11:12:18	176	55	133	0.590	0.501		
Glendale	34.15	-118.25	10:06:25	253	43	–	–	–	–	12:22:15	88	62	11:12:30	176	55	133	0.578	0.487		
Hayward	37.67	-122.08	10:13:50	243	40	–	–	–	–	12:16:31	103	58	11:13:39	176	50	131	0.456	0.348		
Huntington Beach	33.67	-118.08	10:05:19	254	43	–	–	–	–	12:22:09	87	63	11:11:52	177	55	132	0.589	0.500		
Irvine	33.68	-117.77	10:05:31	254	43	–	–	–	–	12:22:53	86	63	11:12:20	176	55	133	0.595	0.506		
Long Beach	33.78	-118.18	10:05:33	254	43	–	–	–	–	12:22:03	88	63	11:11:56	177	55	132	0.585	0.495		
Los Angeles	34.07	-118.25	10:06:13	253	43	–	–	–	–	12:22:10	88	63	11:12:21	176	55	132	0.579	0.488		
Modesto	37.65	-121.00	10:14:06	243	41	–	–	–	–	12:19:00	99	58	11:15:01	175	51	133	0.474	0.368		
Monterey	36.62	-121.92	10:11:13	245	40	–	–	–	–	12:16:04	102	59	11:12:01	178	51	130	0.475	0.369		
Oakland	37.82	-122.27	10:14:10	242	40	–	–	–	–	12:16:12	103	57	11:13:40	176	50	131	0.450	0.342		
Oceanside	33.20	-117.38	10:04:32	256	44	–	–	–	–	12:23:16	85	64	11:11:59	176	56	133	0.610	0.524		
Ontario	34.07	-117.65	10:06:30	253	44	–	–	–	–	12:23:31	86	63	11:13:11	176	55	134	0.590	0.501		
Oxnard	34.25	-119.12	10:06:17	252	42	–	–	–	–	12:20:23	91	62	11:11:30	177	54	131	0.561	0.466		
Pasadena	34.15	-118.15	10:06:28	253	43	–	–	–	–	12:22:28	88	62	11:12:39	176	55	133	0.580	0.489		
Pomona	34.07	-117.75	10:06:27	253	44	–	–	–	–	12:23:18	86	63	11:13:03	176	55	133	0.589	0.499		
Riverside	33.98	-117.37	10:06:26	254	44	–	–	–	–	12:24:04	85	63	11:13:26	175	55	134	0.597	0.509		
Sacramento	38.58	-121.48	10:16:19	241	41	–	–	–	–	12:18:36	101	57	11:16:00	174	50	134	0.452	0.343		
Salinas	36.67	-121.65	10:11:25	245	40	–	–	–	–	12:16:43	101	59	11:12:27	177	51	131	0.478	0.373		
San Bernardino	34.17	-117.27	10:06:57	253	44	–	–	–	–	12:24:28	84	63	11:13:54	175	55	134	0.595	0.507		
San Diego	32.72	-117.15	10:03:29	257	44	–	–	–	–	12:23:17	83	64	11:11:26	177	56	132	0.623	0.539		
San Francisco	37.78	-122.42	10:14:03	242	40	–	–	–	–	12:15:50	104	57	11:13:25	177	50	131	0.448	0.340		
San Jose	37.33	-121.88	10:13:02	244	40	–	–	–	–	12:16:43	102	58	11:13:19	176	50	131	0.464	0.357		
Santa Ana	33.77	-117.87	10:05:40	254	43	–	–	–	–	12:22:44	87	63	11:12:21	176	55	133	0.591	0.502		
Santa Barbara	34.43	-119.73	10:06:29	252	42	–	–	–	–	12:19:09	94	62	11:11:00	178	53	130	0.547	0.450		
Santa Cruz	36.97	-122.02	10:12:04	244	40	–	–	–	–	12:16:07	102	58	11:12:30	177	50	130	0.467	0.361		
Santa Rosa	33.97	-120.10	10:05:11	252	42	–	–	–	–	12:17:52	95	62	11:09:40	179	53	129	0.548	0.452		
Stockton	37.97	-121.28	10:14:49	242	41	–	–	–	–	12:18:36	100	58	11:15:12	175	51	133	0.464	0.357		
Sunnyvale	37.38	-122.03	10:13:08	243	40	–	–	–	–	12:16:25	102	58	11:13:13	177	50	131	0.461	0.353		
Thousand Oaks	34.17	-118.83	10:06:12	253	43	–	–	–	–	12:20:57	90	62	11:11:44	177	54	132	0.567	0.474		
Torrance	33.83	-118.32	10:05:37	254	43	–	–	–	–	12:21:48	88	63	11:11:51	177	55	132	0.582	0.491		

Table 2–2: Local Circumstances for Colorado – Kentucky

Location	Lat °	Long °	First Contact Time h m s	V °	Alt °	Second Contact Time h m s	V °	Third Contact Time h m s	V °	Fourth Contact Time h m s	V °	Alt °	Middle Eclipse Time h m s	V °	Alt °	Azm °	Ecl. Mag.	Ecl. Obs.	FDCL	Durat Total
Colorado																				
Arvada	39.80	-105.08	11:28:14	241	52	–	–	–	–	13:53:53	49	56	12:40:19	146	57	170	0.711	0.648		
Aurora	39.73	-104.87	11:28:16	241	52	–	–	–	–	13:54:15	48	56	12:40:32	146	58	170	0.717	0.654		
Boulder	40.02	-105.28	11:28:32	240	51	–	–	–	–	13:53:37	50	56	12:40:20	147	57	170	0.704	0.638		
Colorado Springs	38.83	-104.82	11:26:24	243	52	–	–	–	–	13:53:53	46	57	12:39:22	146	58	170	0.735	0.677		
Denver	39.73	-104.98	11:28:12	241	52	–	–	–	–	13:54:05	49	56	12:40:25	146	58	170	0.714	0.651		
Fort Collins	40.58	-105.08	11:29:55	239	51	–	–	–	–	13:54:16	51	55	12:41:25	146	57	171	0.696	0.629		
Grand Junction	39.07	-108.55	11:23:55	243	50	–	–	–	–	13:46:50	58	58	12:34:21	154	57	161	0.665	0.590		
Pueblo	38.23	-104.60	11:25:18	244	53	–	–	–	–	13:53:54	45	57	12:38:48	146	59	170	0.751	0.697		
Thornton	39.87	-104.97	11:28:28	240	52	–	–	–	–	13:54:08	49	56	12:40:35	146	57	170	0.712	0.649		
Westminster	39.83	-105.03	11:28:21	240	52	–	–	–	–	13:54:00	49	56	12:40:26	146	57	170	0.712	0.648		
Connecticut																				
Bridgeport	41.18	-73.20	14:12:11	215	52	–	–	–	–	16:37:13	4	31	15:26:49	285	42	236	0.916	0.906		
Hartford	41.77	-72.68	14:13:20	214	51	–	–	–	–	16:37:46	5	30	15:27:40	286	42	236	0.929	0.922		
New Haven	41.30	-72.92	14:12:42	214	52	–	–	–	–	16:37:29	4	30	15:27:13	285	42	236	0.917	0.907		
New London	41.37	-72.10	14:14:01	214	51	–	–	–	–	16:38:11	4	30	15:28:16	285	41	237	0.911	0.900		
Waterbury	41.55	-73.05	14:12:38	214	52	–	–	–	–	16:37:25	5	30	15:27:09	286	42	236	0.926	0.918		
Delaware																				
Dover	39.17	-75.53	14:07:03	218	55	–	–	–	–	16:34:29	359	33	15:22:48	284	46	234	0.881	0.861		
Newark	39.65	-75.77	14:07:00	218	55	–	–	–	–	16:34:28	1	33	15:22:44	285	46	233	0.898	0.883		
Wilmington	39.75	-75.55	14:07:26	217	55	–	–	–	–	16:34:42	1	33	15:23:05	285	45	234	0.898	0.884		
District of Columbia																				
Washington	38.92	-76.98	14:04:23	219	56	–	–	–	–	16:33:00	360	35	15:20:37	285	47	232	0.890	0.873		
Florida																				
Daytona Beach	29.22	-81.02	13:48:12	235	68	–	–	–	–	16:18:52	335	44	15:04:59	275	58	232	0.667	0.593		
Fort Lauderdale	26.12	-80.13	13:48:06	236	70	–	–	–	–	16:14:07	324	45	15:02:30	270	60	237	0.565	0.472		
Fort Myers	26.63	-81.85	13:44:01	241	71	–	–	–	–	16:13:23	328	47	14:59:56	273	61	233	0.609	0.523		
Hialeah	25.83	-80.28	13:47:31	237	71	–	–	–	–	16:13:23	323	46	15:01:48	269	60	237	0.560	0.465		
Hollywood	26.02	-80.15	13:47:59	237	71	–	–	–	–	16:13:54	324	45	15:02:19	270	60	237	0.563	0.469		
Jacksonville	30.33	-81.65	13:47:45	235	67	–	–	–	–	16:19:53	339	44	15:05:15	278	58	230	0.708	0.644		
Melbourne	28.08	-80.62	13:48:15	236	69	–	–	–	–	16:17:22	331	44	15:04:15	273	59	234	0.628	0.547		
Miami	25.78	-80.18	13:47:45	237	71	–	–	–	–	16:13:23	323	45	15:01:56	269	60	237	0.557	0.462		
Orlando	28.55	-81.38	13:46:46	237	69	–	–	–	–	16:17:22	333	45	15:03:27	275	59	232	0.654	0.578		
Pensacola	30.42	-87.22	12:35:59	248	67	–	–	–	–	15:13:26	347	50	13:55:28	286	63	217	0.805	0.765		
Sarasota	27.33	-82.53	13:42:55	242	70	–	–	–	–	16:13:59	331	47	14:59:38	275	61	231	0.640	0.560		
St. Petersburg	27.78	-82.67	13:43:01	242	70	–	–	–	–	16:14:39	332	47	15:00:02	275	61	230	0.654	0.578		
Tallahassee	30.45	-84.28	13:42:07	241	67	–	–	–	–	16:17:04	343	47	15:00:43	281	60	224	0.755	0.702		
Tampa	27.95	-82.45	13:43:41	241	69	–	–	–	–	16:15:10	333	46	15:00:40	275	61	230	0.655	0.579		
West Palm Beach	26.72	-80.05	13:48:42	236	70	–	–	–	–	16:15:24	326	45	15:03:29	271	59	236	0.581	0.490		
Georgia																				
Albany	31.58	-84.17	13:43:39	239	66	–	–	–	–	16:18:45	346	46	15:02:23	283	59	224	0.784	0.738		
Athens	33.95	-83.38	13:47:55	233	63	–	–	–	–	16:22:25	352	43	15:06:30	284	56	224	0.836	0.805		
Atlanta	33.75	-84.38	13:45:47	235	64	–	–	–	–	16:21:02	352	44	15:04:38	286	57	222	0.846	0.818		
Augusta	33.47	-81.97	13:50:10	232	64	–	–	–	–	16:23:32	349	42	15:08:20	282	56	227	0.801	0.760		
Columbus	32.47	-84.98	13:43:03	239	65	–	–	–	–	16:18:52	349	46	15:02:05	285	59	221	0.821	0.786		
Macon	32.85	-83.63	13:46:11	236	65	–	–	–	–	16:20:56	349	44	15:04:51	283	57	224	0.810	0.771		
Marietta	33.95	-84.55	13:45:42	235	64	–	–	–	–	16:21:02	353	45	15:04:35	286	57	221	0.854	0.828		
Peachtree City	33.40	-84.57	13:45:00	236	64	–	–	–	–	16:20:26	352	45	15:03:55	285	58	222	0.839	0.809		
Roswell	34.03	-84.37	13:46:09	235	64	–	–	–	–	16:21:20	353	44	15:04:58	286	57	222	0.854	0.827		
Savannah	32.08	-81.10	13:50:35	232	65	–	–	–	–	16:22:52	344	42	15:08:16	279	56	230	0.749	0.694		
Smyrna	33.88	-84.52	13:45:41	235	64	–	–	–	–	16:21:00	353	45	15:04:33	286	57	222	0.852	0.825		
Valdosta	30.83	-83.28	13:44:40	238	67	–	–	–	–	16:18:46	342	45	15:02:59	280	59	226	0.749	0.694		
Hawaii																				
Hilo	19.73	-155.08	06:28:52	266	4	–	–	–	–	07:57:12	169	25	07:11:32	218	14	87	0.335	0.223		
Honolulu	21.32	-157.87	06:33:34	261	3	–	–	–	–	07:55:00	172	22	07:13:02	217	12	86	0.285	0.177		
Idaho																				
Boise	43.62	-116.22	11:30:28	231	43	–	–	–	–	13:33:13	88	54	12:30:51	162	50	150	0.458	0.350		
Idaho Falls	43.50	-112.03	11:31:56	232	46	–	–	–	–	13:41:54	75	54	12:36:02	156	52	158	0.527	0.427		
Nampa	43.57	-116.57	11:30:12	231	43	–	–	–	–	13:32:27	88	54	12:30:18	162	50	149	0.454	0.346		
Pocatello	42.87	-112.45	11:30:17	233	46	–	–	–	–	13:40:50	75	55	12:34:37	157	53	156	0.530	0.431		
Iowa																				
Ames	42.03	-93.62	12:44:13	230	55	–	–	–	–	15:13:52	29	47	13:59:24	126	54	199	0.850	0.823		
Cedar Rapids	41.98	-91.67	12:46:28	229	55	–	–	–	–	15:16:40	26	45	14:02:07	123	54	203	0.881	0.862		
Council Bluffs	41.27	-95.87	12:40:17	233	55	–	–	–	–	15:10:14	31	49	13:55:24	130	56	193	0.833	0.801		
Davenport	41.53	-90.58	12:47:05	229	56	–	–	–	–	15:18:03	23	45	14:03:13	122	54	205	0.908	0.896		
Des Moines	41.58	-93.62	12:43:27	231	55	–	–	–	–	15:13:45	28	47	13:58:57	126	55	199	0.861	0.837		
Dubuque	42.50	-90.68	12:48:31	227	55	–	–	–	–	15:18:08	25	44	14:03:58	122	53	205	0.882	0.864		
Iowa City	41.67	-91.53	12:46:07	229	56	–	–	–	–	15:16:46	25	46	14:02:00	123	54	203	0.891	0.874		
Sioux City	42.50	-96.40	12:41:59	231	54	–	–	–	–	15:09:47	35	48	13:56:00	131	55	192	0.796	0.754		
Waterloo	42.50	-92.35	12:46:31	228	55	–	–	–	–	15:15:49	28	46	14:01:39	125	53	201	0.858	0.833		
Kansas																				
Kansas City	39.12	-94.63	12:37:51	237	57	–	–	–	–	15:11:14	23	50	13:54:44	127	58	196	0.904	0.891		
Lawrence	38.97	-95.23	12:36:49	238	57	–	–	–	–	15:10:13	24	50	13:53:39	128	58	195	0.898	0.883		
Olathe	38.88	-94.82	12:37:12	238	57	–	–	–	–	15:10:49	23	50	13:54:10	127	58	196	0.907	0.895		
Overland Park	38.97	-94.67	12:37:32	238	57	–	–	–	–	15:11:05	23	50	13:54:30	127	58	196	0.907	0.895		
Topeka	39.05	-95.67	12:36:27	238	57	–	–	–	–	15:09:36	25	51	13:53:07	129	58	194	0.889	0.872		
Wichita	37.70	-97.33	12:31:54	243	57	–	–	–	–	15:06:10	25	53	13:48:53	132	60	189	0.891	0.875		
Kentucky																				
Bowling Green	36.98	-86.45	12:46:18	233	61	–	–	–	–	15:21:18	4	44	14:04:51	292	56	216	0.966	0.967		
Henderson	37.83	-87.58	12:45:41	233	60	14:02:40.5	78	14:05:12.8	151	15:20:25	8	45	14:03:59	294	56	213	1.054	1.000	-0.800	02m28s
Lexington	38.05	-84.50	13:50:53	229	59	–	–	–	–	16:24:24	5	42	15:08:54	291	53	219	0.965	0.967		
Louisville	38.25	-85.77	13:49:07	230	59	–	–	–	–	16:22:58	7	43	15:07:10	292	54	217	0.989	0.993		
Owensboro	37.77	-87.12	12:46:19	232	60	–	–	–	–	15:20:58	7	45	14:04:37	294	55	214	0.996	0.999		
Paducah	37.08	-88.62	12:42:58	235	60	14:00:41.1	92	14:02:23.3	138	15:18:34	8	46	14:01:35	295	57	211	1.055	1.000	-0.920	01m38s

Table 2–3: Local Circumstances for Illinois, Indiana & Louisiana

Location	Lat	Long	First Contact Time	V	Alt	Second Contact Time	V	Third Contact Time	V	Fourth Contact Time	V	Alt	Middle Eclipse Time	V	Alt	Azm	Ecl. Mag.	Ecl. Obs.	FDCL	Durat Total
	°	°	h m s	°	°	h m s	°	h m s	°	h m s	°	°	h m s	°	°	°				
Illinois																				
Aurora	41.75	-88.32	12:50:22	226	56	–	–	–	–	15:21:07	20	43	14:06:37	119	52	210	0.936	0.931		
Bloomington	40.48	-89.00	12:47:33	229	57	–	–	–	–	15:19:51	18	44	14:04:30	119	54	209	0.958	0.959		
Bolingbrook	41.73	-88.05	12:50:42	226	56	–	–	–	–	15:21:28	20	43	14:06:59	118	52	211	0.940	0.936		
Carbondale	37.73	-89.22	12:43:02	235	60	13:59:16.6	25	14:03:25.8	209	15:18:11	10	46	14:01:22	117	57	209	1.054	1.000	0.044	04m08
Centralia	38.53	-89.13	12:44:23	233	59	14:00:58.2	339	14:03:43.0	256	15:18:46	12	46	14:02:21	117	56	209	1.054	1.000	0.754	02m42
Champaign	40.12	-88.25	12:48:02	229	57	–	–	–	–	15:20:42	15	44	14:05:15	117	54	211	0.979	0.982		
Chicago	41.88	-87.63	12:51:29	226	56	–	–	–	–	15:22:03	19	42	14:07:42	118	52	211	0.942	0.938		
Cicero	41.85	-87.75	12:51:16	226	56	–	–	–	–	15:21:53	20	43	14:07:30	118	52	211	0.941	0.937		
Danville	40.13	-87.62	12:48:57	229	57	–	–	–	–	15:21:31	15	43	14:06:11	117	54	212	0.988	0.991		
Decatur	39.85	-88.95	12:46:39	230	58	–	–	–	–	15:19:40	16	45	14:03:58	118	54	209	0.975	0.979		
Downers Grove	41.82	-88.02	12:50:52	226	56	–	–	–	–	15:21:32	20	43	14:07:06	119	52	211	0.938	0.934		
East St. Louis	38.62	-90.12	12:43:05	234	59	–	–	–	–	15:17:29	14	47	14:00:57	119	56	207	0.989	0.993		
Effingham	39.12	-88.55	12:46:07	231	58	14:03:25.2	308	14:03:50.9	285	15:19:51	13	45	14:03:49	117	55	210	1.054	1.000	0.981	00m48
Elgin	42.03	-88.28	12:50:50	226	56	–	–	–	–	15:21:14	21	43	14:06:55	119	52	210	0.929	0.922		
Evanston	42.05	-87.68	12:51:39	225	56	–	–	–	–	15:22:00	20	42	14:07:46	118	52	211	0.937	0.932		
Herrin	37.80	-89.03	12:43:24	234	60	13:59:38.0	27	14:03:47.0	206	15:18:29	10	46	14:01:43	116	57	210	1.054	1.000	0.001	04m08
Joliet	41.53	-88.08	12:50:22	227	56	–	–	–	–	15:21:22	19	43	14:06:46	118	52	211	0.945	0.942		
Kankakee	41.12	-87.87	12:50:02	227	56	–	–	–	–	15:21:32	18	43	14:06:42	118	53	211	0.958	0.959		
Marion	37.73	-88.93	12:43:27	235	60	13:59:43.4	34	14:03:50.2	199	15:18:34	10	46	14:01:48	296	57	210	1.054	1.000	-0.120	04m07
Mount Prospect	42.07	-87.93	12:51:21	226	56	–	–	–	–	15:21:41	20	43	14:07:26	119	52	211	0.933	0.927		
Mount Vernon	38.32	-88.92	12:44:22	233	59	14:00:34.8	2	14:04:15.3	231	15:18:57	11	46	14:02:27	117	56	210	1.054	1.000	0.424	03m44
Naperville	41.77	-88.15	12:50:37	226	56	–	–	–	–	15:21:21	20	43	14:06:52	119	52	210	0.937	0.933		
Oak Lawn	41.72	-87.73	12:51:06	226	56	–	–	–	–	15:21:52	19	43	14:07:25	118	52	211	0.945	0.942		
Oak Park	41.88	-87.78	12:51:16	226	56	–	–	–	–	15:21:51	20	43	14:07:29	118	52	211	0.940	0.936		
Peoria	40.70	-89.60	12:47:04	229	57	–	–	–	–	15:19:07	19	45	14:03:50	120	54	208	0.944	0.941		
Quincy	39.93	-91.38	12:43:27	233	57	–	–	–	–	15:16:22	20	47	14:00:28	122	56	204	0.936	0.932		
Rockford	42.27	-89.10	12:50:08	226	55	–	–	–	–	15:20:13	23	43	14:05:59	120	52	208	0.911	0.900		
Schaumburg	42.03	-88.08	12:51:06	226	56	–	–	–	–	15:21:29	20	43	14:07:11	119	52	210	0.932	0.926		
Skokie	42.05	-87.75	12:51:34	225	56	–	–	–	–	15:21:55	20	42	14:07:40	118	52	211	0.936	0.931		
Springfield	39.80	-89.65	12:45:36	231	58	–	–	–	–	15:18:42	17	45	14:02:53	119	55	208	0.966	0.968		
Wheaton	41.87	-88.10	12:50:50	226	56	–	–	–	–	15:21:26	20	43	14:07:01	119	52	210	0.936	0.931		
Indiana																				
Anderson	40.17	-85.68	13:51:49	227	57	15:07:14.4	358	15:10:45.3	231	16:23:58	12	42	15:09:02	114	52	216	1.054	1.000	0.456	03m34
Bedford	38.87	-86.48	13:48:50	230	59	15:04:46.6	48	15:08:30.9	179	16:22:24	10	43	15:06:40	294	54	215	1.054	1.000	-0.406	03m43
Beech Grove	39.73	-86.05	13:50:41	228	58	15:06:08.2	12	15:10:02.2	216	16:23:20	11	42	15:08:07	114	53	215	1.054	1.000	0.217	03m56
Bloomington	39.17	-86.53	13:49:10	229	58	15:04:50.8	30	15:08:53.8	199	16:22:29	10	43	15:06:53	294	54	215	1.054	1.000	-0.083	04m02
Brownsburg	39.88	-86.38	13:50:24	228	58	15:06:03.1	352	15:09:24.3	237	16:22:59	12	43	15:07:45	115	53	215	1.054	1.000	0.544	03m23
Carmel	39.98	-86.13	13:50:54	227	58	15:06:28.0	354	15:09:53.8	235	16:23:20	12	42	15:08:13	114	53	215	1.054	1.000	0.510	03m27
Columbus	39.22	-85.92	13:50:11	228	58	15:05:55.2	46	15:09:42.3	181	16:23:16	10	43	15:07:51	293	53	216	1.054	1.000	-0.368	03m45
Connersville	39.63	-85.15	13:51:54	227	58	15:07:25.7	45	15:11:11.8	181	16:24:24	10	42	15:09:21	293	53	217	1.054	1.000	-0.360	03m44
Crawfordsville	40.03	-86.90	13:49:51	228	58	15:06:38.6	310	15:07:18.1	281	16:22:24	13	43	15:07:08	115	53	213	1.054	1.000	0.968	01m00
Elkhart	41.68	-85.97	13:53:28	225	56	–	–	–	–	16:24:05	17	41	15:09:52	116	51	215	0.970	0.972		
Evansville	37.97	-87.58	12:45:52	232	60	14:02:35.0	67	14:05:38.0	162	15:20:30	9	45	14:04:07	294	56	213	1.054	1.000	-0.670	03m03
Fishers	39.95	-86.02	13:51:02	227	58	15:06:31.7	0	15:10:07.3	228	16:23:28	12	42	15:08:21	114	53	215	1.054	1.000	0.415	03m39
Fort Wayne	41.07	-85.15	13:53:48	225	56	–	–	–	–	16:24:55	14	41	15:10:32	114	51	216	0.998	0.999		
Frankfort	40.28	-86.52	13:50:45	227	57	–	–	–	–	16:22:58	14	42	15:07:55	115	53	214	1.000	0.999		
Franklin	39.48	-86.05	13:50:20	228	58	15:05:51.8	26	15:09:54.1	202	16:23:14	11	43	15:07:53	294	53	215	1.054	1.000	-0.031	04m02
Gary	41.60	-87.33	12:51:28	226	56	–	–	–	–	15:22:22	18	42	14:07:53	117	52	212	0.953	0.953		
Greenfield	39.78	-85.77	13:51:10	227	58	15:06:34.2	18	15:10:32.6	210	16:23:43	11	42	15:08:34	114	53	216	1.054	1.000	0.117	03m59
Greensburg	39.33	-85.48	13:51:00	228	58	15:06:48.5	52	15:10:20.8	174	16:23:52	10	42	15:08:35	293	53	217	1.054	1.000	-0.484	03m31
Greenwood	39.62	-86.12	13:50:25	228	58	15:05:54.5	17	15:09:52.7	211	16:23:12	11	43	15:07:55	114	53	215	1.054	1.000	0.137	03m59
Hammond	41.63	-87.50	12:51:18	226	56	–	–	–	–	15:22:09	19	42	14:07:40	118	52	212	0.950	0.949		
Indianapolis	39.77	-86.15	13:50:35	228	58	15:06:05.2	7	15:09:52.1	222	16:23:14	12	42	15:08:00	114	53	215	1.054	1.000	0.306	03m50
Jasper	38.40	-86.93	13:47:30	231	59	15:03:55.5	62	15:07:09.8	166	16:21:35	9	44	15:05:33	294	55	214	1.054	1.000	-0.615	03m13
Kokomo	40.48	-86.13	13:51:35	227	57	–	–	–	–	16:23:31	14	42	15:08:39	115	52	215	1.000	0.999		
Lafayette	40.42	-86.90	13:50:23	227	57	–	–	–	–	16:22:32	14	43	15:07:29	116	53	213	0.991	0.994		
Lawrence	39.83	-86.03	13:50:50	228	58	15:06:18.6	7	15:10:05.0	222	16:23:24	12	42	15:08:14	114	53	215	1.054	1.000	0.308	03m49
Lebanon	40.05	-86.47	13:50:30	228	58	15:06:26.1	336	15:09:07.3	254	16:22:57	13	43	15:07:47	115	53	214	1.054	1.000	0.753	02m39
Marion	40.53	-85.67	13:52:20	226	57	15:08:10.7	330	15:10:31.5	259	16:24:07	13	42	15:09:22	114	52	216	1.054	1.000	0.814	02m19
Martinsville	39.43	-86.42	13:49:43	229	58	15:05:17.3	18	15:09:17.1	210	16:22:45	11	43	15:07:18	114	53	215	1.054	1.000	0.117	04m01
Michigan City	41.72	-86.90	13:52:14	225	56	–	–	–	–	16:22:56	18	42	15:08:35	117	52	213	0.956	0.956		
Muncie	40.20	-85.38	13:52:18	226	57	15:07:37.1	5	15:11:19.6	223	16:24:21	12	42	15:09:30	114	52	216	1.054	1.000	0.335	03m46
New Castle	39.92	-85.37	13:51:57	227	58	15:07:15.7	22	15:11:16.1	205	16:24:15	11	42	15:09:16	114	52	217	1.054	1.000	0.039	04m00
New Haven	41.07	-85.02	13:53:59	225	56	–	–	–	–	16:25:04	14	41	15:10:43	114	51	217	1.000	0.999		
Noblesville	40.05	-86.02	13:51:10	227	58	15:06:42.0	354	15:10:07.0	235	16:23:30	12	42	15:08:26	114	53	215	1.054	1.000	0.515	03m26
Plainfield	39.70	-86.40	13:50:07	228	58	15:05:42.1	3	15:09:22.9	226	16:22:53	12	43	15:07:34	115	53	215	1.054	1.000	0.371	03m44
Richmond	39.83	-84.90	13:52:33	226	58	15:07:55.4	40	15:11:45.9	186	16:24:47	10	41	15:09:53	293	52	218	1.054	1.000	-0.290	03m50
Seymour	38.97	-85.88	13:49:54	229	59	15:06:05.4	63	15:09:13.9	163	16:23:12	9	43	15:07:40	293	54	216	1.054	1.000	-0.634	03m08
Shelbyville	39.52	-85.78	13:50:47	228	58	15:06:17.7	32	15:10:17.3	195	16:23:34	11	42	15:08:19	294	53	216	1.054	1.000	-0.141	03m59
South Bend	41.68	-86.25	13:53:05	225	56	–	–	–	–	16:23:44	17	41	15:09:29	116	51	214	0.966	0.968		
Speedway	39.78	-86.25	13:50:27	228	58	15:06:00.0	3	15:09:40.3	226	16:23:07	12	43	15:07:52	114	53	215	1.054	1.000	0.374	03m44
Terre Haute	39.47	-87.42	13:48:17	230	58	15:04:22.9	342	15:07:19.3	249	16:21:30	12	44	15:05:52	116	54	213	1.054	1.000	0.694	02m55
Vincennes	38.68	-87.53	13:46:59	231	59	15:02:51.9	26	15:06:57.6	204	16:20:58	10	44	15:04:55	295	55	213	1.054	1.000	-0.005	04m05
Washington	38.67	-87.17	13:47:31	231	59	15:03:25.4	38	15:07:24.7	191	16:21:25	10	44	15:05:27	295	55	213	1.054	1.000	-0.225	03m58
Louisiana																				
Alexandria	31.30	-92.45	12:27:33	255	64	–	–	–	–	15:07:33	358	54	13:47:40	299	65	202	0.923	0.916		
Baton Rouge	30.45	-91.18	12:28:25	255	65	–	–	–	–	15:08:13	353	53	13:48:33	295	65	206	0.878	0.859		
Bossier City	32.52	-93.73	12:27:29	253	63	–	–	–	–	15:07:08	4	54	13:47:19	303	64	198	0.977	0.980		
Lafayette	30.23	-92.02	12:26:34	257	65	–	–	–	–	15:06:45	354	54	13:46:46	297	66	203	0.889	0.872		
Lake Charles	30.23	-93.22	12:24:28	259	64	–	–	–	–	15:05:02	357	56	13:44:42	301	66	199	0.912	0.902		
Metairie	29.97	-90.17	12:29:34	255	66	–	–	–	–	15:08:57	350	53	13:49:36	292	65	209	0.847	0.819		
Monroe	32.50	-92.12	12:30:06	251	63	–	–	–	–	15:09:29	1	53	13:50:00	299	63	203	0.947	0.945		
New Orleans	29.97	-90.07	12:29:46	255	66	–	–	–	–	15:09:05	350	53	13:49:47	292	65	209	0.845	0.817		
Shreveport	32.52	-93.75	12:27:27	253	63	–	–	–	–	15:07:07	4	54	13:47:18	303	64	198	0.977	0.981		

Table 2–4: Local Circumstances for Maine – Missouri

Location	Lat °	Long °	First Contact Time h m s	V °	Alt °	Second Contact Time h m s	V °	Third Contact Time h m s	V °	Fourth Contact Time h m s	V °	Alt °	Middle Eclipse Time h m s	V °	Alt °	Azm °	Ecl. Mag.	Ecl. Obs.	FDCL	Durat Total
Maine																				
Augusta	44.32	-69.78	14:18:54	210	48	–	–	–	–	16:40:05	11	27	15:31:37	288	38	238	0.980	0.983		
Bangor	44.80	-68.77	14:20:30	210	47	–	–	–	–	16:40:45	12	26	15:32:46	288	37	239	0.987	0.990		
Lewiston	44.10	-70.22	14:18:12	211	48	–	–	–	–	16:39:47	11	27	15:31:07	288	38	238	0.977	0.980		
Portland	43.65	-70.27	14:17:54	211	48	–	–	–	–	16:39:47	9	27	15:31:00	287	39	238	0.964	0.965		
Maryland																				
Annapolis	38.98	-76.50	14:05:16	219	56	–	–	–	–	16:33:29	360	34	15:21:21	284	47	233	0.887	0.869		
Baltimore	39.28	-76.62	14:05:18	219	56	–	–	–	–	16:33:31	1	34	15:21:21	285	46	232	0.897	0.882		
Columbia	39.23	-76.83	14:04:54	219	56	–	–	–	–	16:33:17	1	35	15:21:01	285	47	232	0.898	0.883		
Cumberland	39.65	-78.77	14:02:02	220	56	–	–	–	–	16:31:32	3	36	15:18:34	287	48	229	0.933	0.927		
Hagerstown	39.65	-77.72	14:03:46	219	56	–	–	–	–	16:32:35	3	35	15:20:02	286	47	230	0.920	0.912		
Salisbury	38.37	-75.60	14:06:22	219	56	–	–	–	–	16:34:03	357	34	15:22:15	283	46	234	0.858	0.832		
Towson	39.40	-76.60	14:05:25	219	56	–	–	–	–	16:33:35	1	34	15:21:27	285	46	232	0.900	0.886		
Massachusetts																				
Boston	42.37	-71.07	14:16:07	212	50	–	–	–	–	16:39:09	6	28	15:29:49	286	40	238	0.932	0.926		
Cambridge	42.37	-71.10	14:16:04	212	50	–	–	–	–	16:39:07	6	28	15:29:46	286	40	238	0.932	0.926		
Fall River	41.70	-71.15	14:15:39	213	51	–	–	–	–	16:39:01	4	29	15:29:32	285	40	238	0.912	0.901		
Lowell	42.63	-71.32	14:15:52	212	50	–	–	–	–	16:38:58	7	28	15:29:35	286	40	237	0.942	0.939		
Lynn	42.47	-70.95	14:16:20	212	50	–	–	–	–	16:39:15	6	28	15:29:58	286	40	238	0.934	0.928		
New Bedford	41.63	-70.93	14:15:58	213	51	–	–	–	–	16:39:10	4	28	15:29:47	285	40	239	0.908	0.896		
Newton	42.35	-71.20	14:15:54	212	50	–	–	–	–	16:39:02	6	28	15:29:39	286	40	238	0.933	0.927		
Quincy	42.25	-71.00	14:16:09	212	50	–	–	–	–	16:39:11	6	28	15:29:52	286	40	238	0.928	0.920		
Somerville	42.38	-71.10	14:16:04	212	50	–	–	–	–	16:39:07	6	28	15:29:46	286	40	238	0.933	0.927		
Springfield	42.10	-72.58	14:13:41	213	51	–	–	–	–	16:37:53	6	30	15:27:54	286	41	236	0.938	0.933		
Worcester	42.27	-71.80	14:14:58	213	50	–	–	–	–	16:38:33	6	29	15:28:55	286	41	237	0.936	0.930		
Michigan																				
Ann Arbor	42.28	-83.75	13:57:21	222	55	–	–	–	–	16:26:51	16	39	15:13:23	114	49	219	0.983	0.987		
Battle Creek	42.32	-85.18	13:55:24	223	55	–	–	–	–	16:25:10	18	40	15:11:27	116	50	216	0.964	0.965		
Benton Harbor	42.10	-86.45	13:53:23	224	55	–	–	–	–	16:23:34	19	41	15:09:31	117	51	214	0.952	0.951		
Detroit	42.33	-83.05	13:58:23	221	55	–	–	–	–	16:27:39	15	38	15:14:22	114	49	220	0.991	0.994		
Flint	43.02	-83.68	13:58:21	221	54	–	–	–	–	16:27:01	18	39	15:13:58	115	49	218	0.964	0.965		
Grand Rapids	42.97	-85.67	13:55:37	222	55	–	–	–	–	16:24:40	20	40	15:11:15	117	50	215	0.940	0.936		
Jackson	42.25	-84.40	13:56:23	222	55	–	–	–	–	16:26:04	17	40	15:12:28	115	50	217	0.976	0.979		
Kalamazoo	42.28	-85.58	13:54:49	223	55	–	–	–	–	16:24:41	18	41	15:10:52	116	50	215	0.959	0.959		
Lansing	42.73	-84.55	13:56:49	222	55	–	–	–	–	16:25:59	18	39	15:12:36	115	49	217	0.961	0.961		
Muskegon	43.23	-86.27	13:55:12	222	54	–	–	–	–	16:23:57	21	41	15:10:37	118	50	213	0.925	0.917		
Port Huron	42.97	-82.43	14:00:00	220	54	–	–	–	–	16:28:25	16	38	15:15:36	114	48	220	0.981	0.984		
Saginaw	43.43	-83.93	13:58:32	220	54	–	–	–	–	16:26:45	19	39	15:13:54	116	48	218	0.949	0.948		
Sault Ste. Marie	46.48	-84.35	14:01:54	216	51	–	–	–	–	16:26:01	28	37	15:15:05	119	46	216	0.862	0.838		
Warren	42.52	-83.03	13:58:38	221	55	–	–	–	–	16:27:41	16	38	15:14:30	114	49	220	0.986	0.990		
Minnesota																				
Bloomington	44.83	-93.28	12:49:25	224	52	–	–	–	–	15:14:43	36	45	14:02:29	127	51	199	0.788	0.744		
Duluth	46.78	-92.12	12:53:54	220	51	–	–	–	–	15:16:12	39	42	14:05:34	127	49	201	0.757	0.705		
Minneapolis	44.98	-93.27	12:49:42	224	52	–	–	–	–	15:14:45	36	45	14:02:39	127	51	199	0.785	0.739		
Rochester	44.02	-92.47	12:48:55	225	53	–	–	–	–	15:15:50	32	45	14:02:52	126	52	201	0.819	0.783		
St. Cloud	45.57	-94.15	12:49:49	223	52	–	–	–	–	15:13:28	39	45	14:01:59	129	51	197	0.758	0.706		
St. Paul	44.95	-93.12	12:49:48	224	52	–	–	–	–	15:14:57	36	44	14:02:49	127	51	199	0.788	0.743		
Mississippi																				
Biloxi	30.40	-88.88	12:32:40	251	66	–	–	–	–	15:11:16	349	51	13:52:31	290	64	212	0.834	0.803		
Greenville	33.40	-91.07	12:33:18	247	63	–	–	–	–	15:11:58	1	51	13:53:02	297	62	206	0.950	0.949		
Gulfport	30.37	-89.10	12:32:12	252	66	–	–	–	–	15:10:56	349	51	13:52:05	290	64	212	0.838	0.807		
Jackson	32.30	-90.20	12:33:04	249	64	–	–	–	–	15:11:57	357	51	13:52:59	293	63	208	0.907	0.895		
Meridian	32.37	-88.70	12:35:52	246	65	–	–	–	–	15:14:02	354	50	13:55:36	291	62	212	0.882	0.863		
Pascagoula	30.35	-88.55	12:33:15	251	67	–	–	–	–	15:11:38	348	51	13:53:01	289	64	213	0.827	0.794		
Missouri																				
Cape Girardeau	37.32	-89.53	12:41:55	236	60	13:58:19.7	37	14:02:26.2	197	15:17:29	10	47	14:00:24	297	57	209	1.055	1.000	-0.162	04m06s
Columbia	38.95	-92.33	12:40:33	236	58	–	–	–	–	15:14:33	19	48	13:57:59	123	57	202	0.946	0.943		
Farmington	37.78	-90.42	12:41:19	236	59	13:58:16.9	337	14:00:50.9	261	15:16:35	12	47	13:59:34	119	57	206	1.055	1.000	0.793	02m32s
Independence	39.10	-94.42	12:38:05	237	57	–	–	–	–	15:11:32	23	50	13:55:02	126	58	197	0.908	0.896		
Jackson	37.38	-89.67	12:41:49	236	60	13:58:11.0	29	14:02:21.2	205	15:17:21	10	47	14:00:16	297	57	208	1.055	1.000	-0.021	04m10s
Joplin	37.10	-94.52	12:34:23	242	59	–	–	–	–	15:10:10	18	51	13:52:25	126	60	196	0.954	0.954		
Kansas City	39.10	-94.58	12:37:53	237	57	–	–	–	–	15:11:18	23	50	13:54:47	127	58	196	0.905	0.893		
Kennett	36.23	-90.05	12:39:26	239	61	13:57:10.7	87	13:59:24.7	147	15:16:00	7	48	13:58:20	297	59	208	1.055	1.000	-0.864	02m07s
Poplar Bluff	36.77	-90.40	12:39:44	238	60	13:56:19.6	38	14:00:27.9	198	15:15:55	9	48	13:58:25	298	58	207	1.055	1.000	-0.159	04m08s
Sikeston	36.88	-89.58	12:41:10	237	60	13:58:03.7	60	14:01:36.7	173	15:17:07	8	47	13:59:50	297	58	209	1.055	1.000	-0.539	03m31s
Springfield	37.22	-93.28	12:36:18	240	59	–	–	–	–	15:12:07	16	50	13:54:29	123	59	199	0.972	0.975		
St. Joseph	39.70	-94.87	12:38:36	236	57	–	–	–	–	15:11:10	25	50	13:55:04	127	57	196	0.886	0.869		
St. Louis	38.63	-90.25	12:42:55	234	59	–	–	–	–	15:17:19	14	47	14:00:46	119	56	207	0.987	0.990		
West Plains	36.73	-91.85	12:37:31	240	60	13:54:33.7	347	13:57:37.6	254	15:13:51	12	49	13:56:06	120	59	203	1.055	1.000	0.690	03m03s
Cape Girardeau	37.32	-89.53	12:41:55	236	60	13:58:19.7	37	14:02:26.2	197	15:17:29	10	47	14:00:24	297	57	209	1.055	1.000	-0.162	04m06s
Columbia	38.95	-92.33	12:40:33	236	58	–	–	–	–	15:14:33	19	48	13:57:59	123	57	202	0.946	0.943		
Farmington	37.78	-90.42	12:41:19	236	59	13:58:16.9	337	14:00:50.9	261	15:16:35	12	47	13:59:34	119	57	206	1.055	1.000	0.793	02m32s
Independence	39.10	-94.42	12:38:05	237	57	–	–	–	–	15:11:32	23	50	13:55:02	126	58	197	0.908	0.896		
Jackson	37.38	-89.67	12:41:49	236	60	13:58:11.0	29	14:02:21.2	205	15:17:21	10	47	14:00:16	297	57	208	1.055	1.000	-0.021	04m10s
Joplin	37.10	-94.52	12:34:23	242	59	–	–	–	–	15:10:10	18	51	13:52:25	126	60	196	0.954	0.954		
Kansas City	39.10	-94.58	12:37:53	237	57	–	–	–	–	15:11:18	23	50	13:54:47	127	58	196	0.905	0.893		
Kennett	36.23	-90.05	12:39:26	239	61	13:57:10.7	87	13:59:24.7	147	15:16:00	7	48	13:58:20	297	59	208	1.055	1.000	-0.864	02m07s
Poplar Bluff	36.77	-90.40	12:39:44	238	60	13:56:19.6	38	14:00:27.9	198	15:15:55	9	48	13:58:25	298	58	207	1.055	1.000	-0.159	04m08s
Sikeston	36.88	-89.58	12:41:10	237	60	13:58:03.7	60	14:01:36.7	173	15:17:07	8	47	13:59:50	297	58	209	1.055	1.000	-0.539	03m31s
Springfield	37.22	-93.28	12:36:18	240	59	–	–	–	–	15:12:07	16	50	13:54:29	123	59	199	0.972	0.975		
St. Joseph	39.70	-94.87	12:38:36	236	57	–	–	–	–	15:11:10	25	50	13:55:04	127	57	196	0.886	0.869		
St. Louis	38.63	-90.25	12:42:55	234	59	–	–	–	–	15:17:19	14	47	14:00:46	119	56	207	0.987	0.990		
West Plains	36.73	-91.85	12:37:31	240	60	13:54:33.7	347	13:57:37.6	254	15:13:51	12	49	13:56:06	120	59	203	1.055	1.000	0.690	03m03s

Table 2–5: Local Circumstances for Montana – New York

Location	Lat	Long	First Contact Time	V	Alt	Second Contact Time	V	Third Contact Time	V	Fourth Contact Time	V	Alt	Middle Eclipse Time	V	Alt	Azm	Ecl. Mag.	Ecl. Obs.	FDCL	Durat Total
	°	°	h m s	°	°	h m s	°	h m s	°	h m s	°	°	h m s	°	°	°				
Montana																				
Billings	45.78	-108.50	11:39:01	227	47	–	–	–	–	13:49:26	69	51	12:43:37	149	51	167	0.541	0.443		
Bozeman	45.68	-111.03	11:37:27	227	45	–	–	–	–	13:44:30	76	52	12:40:15	153	51	162	0.505	0.402		
Butte	46.00	-112.53	11:37:35	226	44	–	–	–	–	13:41:36	80	52	12:38:50	155	50	159	0.475	0.369		
Great Falls	47.50	-111.28	11:41:31	223	44	–	–	–	–	13:44:17	79	50	12:42:16	152	49	163	0.469	0.363		
Helena	46.60	-112.03	11:39:09	225	44	–	–	–	–	13:42:42	80	51	12:40:14	154	50	161	0.473	0.367		
Missoula	46.87	-114.02	11:38:59	224	43	–	–	–	–	13:38:46	85	51	12:38:08	156	49	157	0.440	0.330		
Nebraska																				
Bellevue	41.15	-95.90	12:40:02	233	55	–	–	–	–	15:10:09	31	49	13:55:13	130	56	193	0.836	0.804		
Grand Island	40.92	-98.35	12:36:55	235	54	–	–	–	–	15:06:10	35	51	13:51:26	134	56	187	0.801	0.761		
Kearney	40.70	-99.08	12:35:44	236	54	–	–	–	–	15:04:52	36	52	13:50:07	135	57	186	0.794	0.752		
Lincoln	40.82	-96.68	12:38:32	235	55	–	–	–	–	15:08:49	31	50	13:53:43	131	56	191	0.831	0.798		
Omaha	41.28	-96.02	12:40:09	233	55	–	–	–	–	15:10:02	31	49	13:55:12	130	56	193	0.831	0.798		
Nevada																				
Carson City	39.17	-119.77	10:18:20	240	42	–	–	–	–	12:22:55	95	57	11:19:14	171	51	137	0.470	0.364		
Henderson	36.03	-114.98	10:12:39	249	46	–	–	–	–	12:31:11	76	61	11:20:21	168	56	142	0.605	0.518		
Las Vegas	36.17	-115.15	10:12:54	249	46	–	–	–	–	12:30:57	77	61	11:20:21	169	56	142	0.599	0.512		
North Las Vegas	36.20	-115.12	10:12:59	249	46	–	–	–	–	12:31:02	77	61	11:20:27	168	56	142	0.600	0.512		
Reno	39.52	-119.80	10:19:12	239	42	–	–	–	–	12:23:05	96	57	11:19:46	171	51	138	0.464	0.357		
Sparks	39.53	-119.75	10:19:13	239	42	–	–	–	–	12:23:13	95	57	11:19:51	171	51	138	0.465	0.359		
New Hampshire																				
Concord	43.20	-71.53	14:15:52	212	50	–	–	–	–	16:38:48	9	28	15:29:27	287	40	237	0.961	0.962		
Dover	43.20	-70.88	14:16:48	212	49	–	–	–	–	16:39:19	8	28	15:30:12	287	39	238	0.956	0.955		
Manchester	43.00	-71.47	14:15:51	212	50	–	–	–	–	16:38:51	8	28	15:29:29	287	40	237	0.955	0.954		
Nashua	42.75	-71.47	14:15:43	212	50	–	–	–	–	16:38:51	7	29	15:29:25	286	40	237	0.947	0.945		
Portsmouth	43.08	-70.75	14:16:56	212	49	–	–	–	–	16:39:25	8	28	15:30:20	287	39	238	0.951	0.949		
Rochester	43.30	-70.98	14:16:42	212	49	–	–	–	–	16:39:14	9	28	15:30:07	287	39	237	0.960	0.960		
New Jersey																				
Atlantic City	39.35	-74.45	14:09:00	217	55	–	–	–	–	16:35:33	359	32	15:24:23	284	45	235	0.874	0.853		
Camden	39.93	-75.12	14:08:17	217	54	–	–	–	–	16:35:10	1	33	15:23:46	285	45	234	0.899	0.884		
Clifton	40.88	-74.15	14:10:29	215	53	–	–	–	–	16:36:20	4	31	15:25:29	285	43	235	0.917	0.907		
East Orange	40.77	-74.22	14:10:18	216	53	–	–	–	–	16:36:14	3	32	15:25:21	285	44	235	0.914	0.904		
Elizabeth	40.67	-74.22	14:10:14	216	53	–	–	–	–	16:36:13	3	32	15:25:18	285	44	235	0.911	0.900		
Jersey City	40.73	-74.07	14:10:31	215	53	–	–	–	–	16:36:22	3	31	15:25:32	285	43	235	0.912	0.900		
Newark	40.73	-74.17	14:10:22	216	53	–	–	–	–	16:36:16	3	32	15:25:24	285	43	235	0.913	0.902		
Paterson	40.92	-74.18	14:10:27	215	53	–	–	–	–	16:36:18	4	31	15:25:27	285	43	235	0.918	0.909		
Trenton	40.23	-74.77	14:09:04	216	54	–	–	–	–	16:35:35	2	32	15:24:23	285	44	234	0.904	0.891		
Woodbridge	40.57	-74.28	14:10:04	216	53	–	–	–	–	16:36:07	3	32	15:25:10	285	44	235	0.909	0.897		
New Mexico																				
Alamogordo	32.90	-105.95	11:12:25	259	54	–	–	–	–	13:46:46	39	63	12:28:17	155	63	159	0.834	0.803		
Albuquerque	35.08	-106.65	11:16:33	253	52	–	–	–	–	13:47:35	45	61	12:30:53	154	61	160	0.776	0.729		
Carlsbad	32.42	-104.23	11:13:10	260	55	–	–	–	–	13:49:28	32	63	12:30:08	151	64	164	0.878	0.858		
Clovis	34.40	-103.20	11:18:29	254	55	–	–	–	–	13:53:24	32	60	12:35:00	146	63	169	0.857	0.831		
Las Cruces	32.32	-106.78	11:10:19	260	53	–	–	–	–	13:44:32	41	64	12:26:00	157	63	156	0.830	0.797		
Roswell	33.40	-104.53	11:14:57	257	55	–	–	–	–	13:49:58	35	62	12:31:19	150	63	164	0.852	0.825		
Santa Fe	35.68	-105.95	11:18:31	251	53	–	–	–	–	13:49:28	44	60	12:32:55	151	61	163	0.777	0.731		
New York																				
Albany	42.65	-73.75	14:12:16	214	51	–	–	–	–	16:36:57	8	30	15:26:38	287	42	234	0.966	0.967		
Amherst	42.98	-78.80	14:05:09	217	53	15:18:29.8	14	15:22:12.5	207	16:32:15	13	35	15:20:22	111	45	226	1.052	1.000	0.117	03m44s
Auburn	42.93	-76.57	14:08:20	215	52	15:22:16.4	81	15:24:05.1	137	16:34:25	11	33	15:23:13	289	44	230	1.052	1.000	-0.882	01m45s
Batavia	43.00	-78.18	14:06:03	216	53	15:19:17.7	28	15:23:01.7	193	16:32:52	13	34	15:21:11	290	45	227	1.052	1.000	-0.129	03m42s
Binghamton	42.10	-75.92	14:08:38	216	53	–	–	–	–	16:34:58	8	33	15:23:43	288	44	231	0.972	0.974		
Buffalo	42.88	-78.88	14:04:56	217	53	15:18:20.4	18	15:22:05.4	203	16:32:10	13	35	15:20:14	111	46	226	1.052	1.000	0.046	03m45s
Canandaigua	42.90	-77.28	14:07:16	216	53	15:20:49.3	58	15:23:45.6	161	16:33:44	12	33	15:22:17	290	44	229	1.052	1.000	-0.621	02m55s
Cheektowaga	42.90	-78.75	14:05:08	217	53	15:18:30.6	21	15:22:16.4	201	16:32:18	13	35	15:20:24	111	45	227	1.052	1.000	0.004	03m45s
Depew	42.90	-78.70	14:05:13	217	53	15:18:34.4	22	15:22:20.4	199	16:32:21	13	35	15:20:28	291	45	227	1.052	1.000	-0.017	03m45s
Dunkirk	42.48	-79.33	14:03:53	218	54	15:17:31.8	32	15:21:15.8	189	16:31:40	12	35	15:19:26	291	46	226	1.052	1.000	-0.197	03m43s
Fredonia	42.43	-79.33	14:03:50	218	54	15:17:31.6	35	15:21:12.4	186	16:31:40	12	35	15:19:24	291	46	226	1.052	1.000	-0.251	03m40s
Fulton	43.32	-76.42	14:08:52	215	52	15:21:57.6	51	15:25:07.5	169	16:34:34	12	32	15:23:33	290	44	230	1.052	1.000	-0.511	03m10s
Geneva	42.87	-76.98	14:07:40	216	52	15:21:26.3	71	15:23:47.4	148	16:34:01	11	33	15:22:39	289	44	229	1.052	1.000	-0.784	02m18s
Greece	43.22	-77.68	14:06:58	216	52	15:20:02.3	26	15:23:45.6	194	16:33:22	13	34	15:21:55	290	44	228	1.052	1.000	-0.100	03m42s
Irondequoit	43.22	-77.58	14:07:07	216	52	15:20:10.0	29	15:23:52.5	192	16:33:28	13	33	15:22:02	290	44	228	1.052	1.000	-0.142	03m41s
Jamestown	42.10	-79.23	14:03:39	218	54	15:17:55.3	62	15:20:47.4	159	16:31:43	11	35	15:19:22	290	46	226	1.052	1.000	-0.659	02m51s
Kenmore	42.97	-78.87	14:05:02	217	53	15:18:24.4	14	15:22:06.6	208	16:32:11	13	35	15:20:17	111	46	226	1.052	1.000	0.128	03m43s
Lackawanna	42.83	-78.83	14:04:57	217	53	15:18:22.0	23	15:22:08.4	198	16:32:12	13	35	15:20:16	291	46	227	1.052	1.000	-0.033	03m45s
Lancaster	42.90	-78.67	14:05:16	217	53	15:18:37.0	23	15:22:23.1	198	16:32:23	13	35	15:20:30	291	45	227	1.052	1.000	-0.032	03m45s
Lockport	43.17	-78.70	14:05:28	217	53	15:18:46.6	5	15:22:20.1	217	16:32:22	14	34	15:20:35	111	45	227	1.052	1.000	0.276	03m36s
Massena	44.93	-74.90	14:12:17	212	50	15:24:40.3	333	15:27:06.9	248	16:35:50	16	31	15:25:54	111	41	231	1.051	1.000	0.741	02m25s
Mineola	44.75	-73.65	14:13:50	212	49	15:25:31.2	16	15:29:03.8	204	16:36:56	14	30	15:27:19	110	41	233	1.051	1.000	0.068	03m33s
New York	40.72	-74.00	14:10:37	215	53	–	–	–	–	16:36:25	3	31	15:25:36	285	43	235	0.911	0.899		
Niagara Falls	43.10	-79.05	14:04:55	217	53	15:18:21.4	1	15:21:48.8	222	16:32:01	14	35	15:20:07	111	46	226	1.052	1.000	0.355	03m31s
North Tonawanda	43.03	-78.88	14:05:05	217	53	15:18:26.8	9	15:22:04.8	213	16:32:10	13	35	15:20:17	111	45	226	1.052	1.000	0.208	03m40s
Ogdensburg	44.70	-75.50	14:11:17	213	50	15:23:49.2	337	15:26:25.8	245	16:35:20	15	31	15:25:07	111	42	230	1.051	1.000	0.700	02m35s
Oneida	43.10	-75.65	14:09:48	215	52	–	–	–	–	16:35:16	11	32	15:24:26	289	43	231	0.998	0.999		
Oswego	43.45	-76.52	14:08:50	215	52	15:21:41.3	39	15:25:11.3	181	16:34:29	13	33	15:23:28	290	43	230	1.052	1.000	-0.320	03m29s
Plattsburgh	44.70	-73.47	14:14:03	212	49	15:25:43.0	23	15:29:17.5	196	16:37:06	14	30	15:27:31	290	40	233	1.051	1.000	-0.056	03m33s
Poughkeepsie	41.70	-73.93	14:11:22	215	52	–	–	–	–	16:36:41	6	31	15:26:05	286	43	235	0.939	0.935		
Rochester	43.17	-77.62	14:07:02	216	52	15:20:06.7	31	15:23:47.7	189	16:33:26	13	34	15:21:59	290	44	228	1.052	1.000	-0.182	03m39s
Rome	43.22	-75.45	14:10:11	214	51	–	–	–	–	16:35:28	11	32	15:24:43	289	43	231	1.000	0.999		
Syracuse	43.05	-76.15	14:09:03	215	52	15:23:00.7	86	15:24:31.0	132	16:34:49	11	32	15:23:47	289	43	230	1.052	1.000	-0.920	01m27s
Tonawanda	43.02	-78.88	14:05:04	217	53	15:18:25.9	10	15:22:04.9	212	16:32:10	13	35	15:20:17	111	45	226	1.052	1.000	0.190	03m41s
Utica	43.10	-75.23	14:10:25	214	52	–	–	–	–	16:35:40	11	32	15:24:57	289	43	232	0.994	0.997		
Watertown	43.98	-75.92	14:10:08	214	51	15:22:34.2	18	15:26:12.4	202	16:35:01	14	32	15:24:24	110	43	230	1.051	1.000	0.045	03m39s
West Seneca	42.85	-78.80	14:05:01	217	53	15:18:25.1	23	15:22:11.4	199	16:32:15	13	35	15:20:19	291	46	227	1.052	1.000	-0.029	03m45s
Yonkers	40.93	-73.90	14:10:55	215	53	–	–	–	–	16:36:33	4	31	15:25:49	285	43	235	0.916	0.906		

Table 2–6: Local Circumstances for North Carolina – Oregon

Location	Lat	Long	First Contact Time	V	Alt	Second Contact Time	V	Third Contact Time	V	Fourth Contact Time	V	Alt	Middle Eclipse Time	V	Alt	Azm	Ecl. Mag.	Ecl. Obs.	FDCL	Durat Total
	°	°	h m s	°	°	h m s	°	h m s	°	h m s	°	°	h m s	°	°	°				
North Carolina																				
Asheville	35.60	-82.55	13:51:21	230	62	-	-	-	-	16:24:57	355	42	15:09:37	285	54	224	0.869	0.847		
Charlotte	35.22	-80.85	13:54:07	228	62	-	-	-	-	16:26:30	353	40	15:11:56	283	53	228	0.834	0.802		
Durham	36.00	-78.90	13:58:31	224	60	-	-	-	-	16:29:14	353	38	15:15:41	282	51	231	0.829	0.796		
Fayetteville	35.05	-78.88	13:57:44	225	61	-	-	-	-	16:28:26	350	38	15:14:54	281	52	232	0.802	0.761		
Gastonia	35.27	-81.18	13:53:32	228	62	-	-	-	-	16:26:10	353	41	15:11:26	284	53	227	0.840	0.810		
Greensboro	36.07	-79.80	13:56:54	225	60	-	-	-	-	16:28:21	354	39	15:14:21	283	52	229	0.843	0.814		
Raleigh	35.77	-78.63	13:58:50	224	60	-	-	-	-	16:29:19	352	38	15:15:54	282	51	231	0.819	0.783		
Winston-Salem	36.10	-80.25	13:56:06	226	60	-	-	-	-	16:27:54	355	39	15:13:41	284	52	228	0.851	0.823		
North Dakota																				
Bismarck	46.80	-100.78	12:46:16	224	49	-	-	-	-	15:03:08	54	47	13:54:35	138	51	184	0.636	0.555		
Fargo	46.88	-96.80	12:49:41	222	50	-	-	-	-	15:09:25	47	45	13:59:43	133	50	192	0.691	0.622		
Grand Forks	47.92	-97.05	12:51:21	220	49	-	-	-	-	15:08:52	50	45	14:00:16	134	49	192	0.665	0.590		
Minot	48.23	-101.30	12:48:43	221	48	-	-	-	-	15:02:09	58	46	13:55:19	139	49	183	0.599	0.511		
Ohio																				
Akron	41.08	-81.52	13:59:11	221	56	15:14:14.2	65	15:17:02.8	157	16:29:06	10	38	15:15:39	291	49	223	1.053	1.000	-0.692	02m48s
Alliance	40.92	-81.10	13:59:37	221	56	-	-	-	-	16:29:30	9	37	15:16:07	290	49	224	0.998	0.999		
Ashtabula	41.87	-80.78	14:01:07	220	55	15:15:13.5	33	15:19:00.1	189	16:30:04	12	37	15:17:09	291	48	224	1.053	1.000	-0.206	03m45s
Barberton	41.00	-81.65	13:58:53	222	56	15:14:01.3	67	15:16:44.3	155	16:28:55	10	38	15:15:24	291	49	223	1.053	1.000	-0.718	02m42s
Beavercreek	39.73	-84.07	13:53:41	226	58	15:09:48.6	78	15:12:08.1	146	16:25:44	9	41	15:11:01	292	52	219	1.053	1.000	-0.825	02m15s
Bowling Green	41.38	-83.65	13:56:22	223	56	15:11:23.6	342	15:14:21.2	244	16:26:46	13	39	15:12:53	113	50	219	1.053	1.000	0.657	02m57s
Brunswick	41.23	-81.85	13:58:50	221	56	15:13:26.5	44	15:17:03.9	179	16:28:46	11	38	15:15:17	291	49	222	1.053	1.000	-0.376	03m36s
Canton	40.80	-81.38	13:59:04	221	56	-	-	-	-	16:29:11	9	38	15:15:39	290	49	223	0.999	0.999		
Cincinnati	39.10	-84.52	13:52:12	227	58	-	-	-	-	16:24:56	8	41	15:09:49	292	53	219	0.994	0.997		
Cleveland	41.50	-81.70	13:59:22	221	55	15:13:43.9	31	15:17:34.1	192	16:29:00	12	38	15:15:40	291	49	223	1.053	1.000	-0.164	03m49s
Cleveland Height	41.50	-81.57	13:59:34	221	55	15:13:55.2	35	15:17:42.3	188	16:29:08	11	38	15:15:51	291	49	223	1.053	1.000	-0.229	03m46s
Columbus	39.97	-83.00	13:55:38	224	57	-	-	-	-	16:27:05	9	40	15:12:45	291	51	221	0.997	0.999		
Cuyahoga Falls	41.13	-81.48	13:59:17	221	56	15:14:15.1	62	15:17:11.3	159	16:29:08	10	38	15:15:43	291	49	223	1.053	1.000	-0.657	02m55s
Dayton	39.75	-84.20	13:53:30	226	58	15:09:27.4	70	15:12:10.0	154	16:25:36	9	41	15:10:50	292	52	219	1.054	1.000	-0.738	02m41s
Dublin	40.15	-83.15	13:55:36	224	57	15:11:34.4	82	15:13:39.6	141	16:26:58	9	40	15:12:40	291	51	221	1.053	1.000	-0.866	01m58s
East Cleveland	41.55	-81.55	13:59:39	221	55	15:13:57.8	32	15:17:47.1	190	16:29:10	12	38	15:15:54	291	48	223	1.053	1.000	-0.184	03m48s
Elyria	41.37	-82.12	13:58:36	221	56	15:13:03.0	28	15:16:55.9	195	16:28:30	12	38	15:15:00	292	49	222	1.053	1.000	-0.107	03m52s
Euclid	41.57	-81.53	13:59:41	221	55	15:13:59.9	32	15:17:49.4	191	16:29:11	12	38	15:15:56	291	48	223	1.053	1.000	-0.174	03m48s
Fairborn	39.82	-84.03	13:53:51	225	58	15:09:46.8	71	15:12:24.7	152	16:25:49	9	41	15:11:08	292	52	219	1.053	1.000	-0.758	02m36s
Fairfield	39.35	-84.57	13:52:26	227	58	15:09:16.9	95	15:10:27.6	129	16:24:59	9	41	15:09:57	292	52	218	1.054	1.000	-0.954	01m12s
Findlay	41.03	-83.65	13:55:56	223	56	15:10:44.4	6	15:14:26.9	220	16:26:40	12	40	15:12:37	113	50	219	1.053	1.000	0.296	03m45s
Garfield Heights	41.43	-81.62	13:59:25	221	55	15:13:49.8	38	15:17:34.1	185	16:29:04	11	38	15:15:44	291	49	223	1.053	1.000	-0.276	03m43s
Hamilton	39.40	-84.57	13:52:30	227	58	15:09:03.8	87	15:10:52.7	137	16:25:01	9	41	15:10:00	292	52	218	1.054	1.000	-0.902	01m44s
Huber Heights	39.85	-84.13	13:53:44	226	58	15:09:31.4	65	15:12:28.6	159	16:25:42	9	41	15:11:01	292	52	219	1.053	1.000	-0.672	02m57s
Kent	41.15	-81.37	13:59:28	221	56	15:14:29.0	65	15:17:16.6	156	16:29:16	10	38	15:15:54	291	49	223	1.053	1.000	-0.695	02m47s
Kettering	39.68	-84.17	13:53:28	226	58	15:09:37.2	78	15:11:57.1	146	16:25:36	9	41	15:10:49	292	52	219	1.054	1.000	-0.824	02m15s
Lakewood	41.48	-81.80	13:59:12	221	55	15:13:34.3	30	15:17:25.7	193	16:28:53	12	38	15:15:31	292	49	222	1.053	1.000	-0.136	03m50s
Lima	40.73	-84.10	13:54:54	224	57	15:09:50.0	11	15:13:39.5	215	16:26:04	12	40	15:11:46	113	51	219	1.053	1.000	0.216	03m51s
Lorain	41.47	-82.18	13:58:37	221	56	15:13:02.1	20	15:16:55.3	203	16:28:28	12	38	15:14:59	112	49	222	1.053	1.000	0.032	03m53s
Mansfield	40.75	-82.52	13:57:17	223	56	15:12:23.2	56	15:15:39.0	167	16:27:53	10	39	15:14:01	291	50	222	1.053	1.000	-0.559	03m15s
Maple Heights	41.42	-81.57	13:59:28	221	55	15:13:54.8	40	15:17:36.2	182	16:29:07	11	38	15:15:48	291	49	223	1.053	1.000	-0.317	03m40s
Marion	40.58	-83.13	13:56:09	223	57	15:11:12.3	47	15:14:47.3	176	16:27:08	10	39	15:13:01	292	50	221	1.053	1.000	-0.426	03m34s
Massillon	40.80	-81.53	13:58:50	222	56	15:14:55.9	101	15:15:30.1	120	16:29:00	9	38	15:15:26	291	49	223	1.053	1.000	-0.986	00m39s
Mentor	41.67	-81.35	14:00:04	220	55	15:14:18.9	31	15:18:08.8	192	16:29:25	12	37	15:16:15	291	48	223	1.053	1.000	-0.155	03m49s
Middletown	39.52	-84.40	13:52:54	226	58	15:09:15.3	83	15:11:19.9	141	16:25:15	9	41	15:10:21	292	52	219	1.054	1.000	-0.872	01m57s
North Olmsted	41.42	-81.93	13:58:55	221	56	15:13:20.5	30	15:17:12.0	193	16:28:43	12	38	15:15:17	292	49	222	1.053	1.000	-0.142	03m50s
North Royalton	41.32	-81.73	13:59:06	221	56	15:13:38.0	42	15:17:17.8	181	16:28:55	11	38	15:15:30	291	49	223	1.053	1.000	-0.344	03m39s
Parma	41.38	-81.72	13:59:12	221	56	15:13:39.7	38	15:17:23.8	185	16:28:57	11	38	15:15:34	291	49	223	1.053	1.000	-0.281	03m43s
Sandusky	41.45	-82.70	13:57:50	222	56	15:12:21.4	8	15:16:04.8	217	16:27:52	12	39	15:14:15	112	49	221	1.053	1.000	0.262	03m46s
Shaker Heights	41.48	-81.53	13:59:36	221	55	15:13:58.3	37	15:17:43.3	186	16:29:10	11	38	15:15:53	291	49	223	1.053	1.000	-0.263	03m44s
Springfield	39.92	-83.82	13:54:18	225	57	15:10:12.1	72	15:12:48.2	152	16:26:07	9	40	15:11:32	292	51	220	1.053	1.000	-0.764	02m34s
Steubenville	40.37	-80.62	13:59:47	221	56	-	-	-	-	16:29:52	7	37	15:16:26	289	49	225	0.977	0.980		
Stow	41.18	-81.43	13:59:25	221	56	15:14:18.7	60	15:17:21.0	162	16:29:13	10	38	15:15:50	291	49	223	1.053	1.000	-0.628	03m01s
Strongsville	41.32	-81.83	13:58:58	221	56	15:13:27.7	39	15:17:11.1	184	16:28:48	11	38	15:15:22	291	49	222	1.053	1.000	-0.296	03m42s
Toledo	41.65	-83.55	13:56:51	222	56	15:12:16.9	321	15:14:05.2	265	16:26:57	14	39	15:13:13	113	50	219	1.053	1.000	0.885	01m49s
Trotwood	39.80	-84.30	13:53:25	226	58	15:09:10.9	62	15:12:16.2	162	16:25:29	10	41	15:10:44	292	52	219	1.054	1.000	-0.636	03m04s
Upper Arlington	40.00	-83.07	13:55:33	224	57	-	-	-	-	16:27:00	9	40	15:12:40	291	51	221	0.998	0.999		
Warren	41.23	-80.82	14:00:24	220	55	15:15:39.1	81	15:17:40.3	140	16:29:53	10	37	15:16:43	290	48	224	1.053	1.000	-0.868	01m55s
Westerville	40.13	-82.93	13:55:55	224	57	15:12:30.5	104	15:12:58.2	118	16:27:12	9	39	15:12:58	291	51	221	1.053	1.000	-0.993	00m28s
Westlake	41.45	-81.93	13:58:58	221	56	15:13:21.8	28	15:17:14.2	195	16:28:43	12	38	15:15:19	292	49	222	1.053	1.000	-0.107	03m51s
Youngstown	41.10	-80.65	14:00:31	220	56	-	-	-	-	16:30:03	9	37	15:16:52	290	48	225	0.998	0.999		
Oklahoma																				
Broken Arrow	36.05	-95.80	12:30:46	246	59	-	-	-	-	15:07:23	18	53	13:49:01	128	61	192	0.957	0.957		
Edmond	35.65	-97.48	12:27:48	248	58	-	-	-	-	15:04:22	20	55	13:45:49	132	62	187	0.936	0.931		
Enid	36.40	-97.88	12:28:44	246	58	-	-	-	-	15:04:20	23	55	13:46:16	133	61	187	0.911	0.901		
Midwest City	35.45	-97.40	12:27:31	248	59	-	-	-	-	15:04:20	20	55	13:45:40	132	62	188	0.942	0.939		
Norman	35.22	-97.43	12:27:02	249	59	-	-	-	-	15:04:05	19	55	13:45:17	132	62	187	0.947	0.945		
Oklahoma City	35.50	-97.50	12:27:30	248	58	-	-	-	-	15:04:14	20	55	13:45:35	132	62	187	0.939	0.935		
Tulsa	36.17	-95.92	12:30:49	245	59	-	-	-	-	15:07:18	18	53	13:49:00	128	61	192	0.952	0.951		
Oregon																				
Beaverton	45.48	-122.80	10:33:38	224	39	-	-	-	-	12:19:29	108	50	11:25:39	168	46	140	0.332	0.221		
Corvallis	44.57	-123.27	10:31:15	226	39	-	-	-	-	12:18:02	109	51	11:23:40	169	46	138	0.338	0.226		
Eugene	44.08	-123.07	10:30:03	227	39	-	-	-	-	12:18:16	108	52	11:23:09	170	46	138	0.347	0.236		
Gresham	45.50	-122.43	10:33:42	225	39	-	-	-	-	12:20:19	107	51	11:26:06	168	46	141	0.337	0.226		
Hillsboro	45.52	-122.98	10:33:42	224	39	-	-	-	-	12:19:05	108	50	11:25:29	168	45	140	0.329	0.218		
Medford	42.32	-122.87	10:25:33	232	39	-	-	-	-	12:17:49	106	53	11:20:32	171	47	136	0.375	0.263		
Portland	45.53	-122.62	10:33:46	224	39	-	-	-	-	12:19:55	107	50	11:25:56	168	46	141	0.334	0.223		
Salem	44.93	-123.03	10:32:13	226	39	-	-	-	-	12:18:44	108	51	11:24:31	169	46	139	0.336	0.225		
Springfield	44.05	-123.02	10:29:57	228	39	-	-	-	-	12:18:22	108	52	11:23:09	170	46	138	0.349	0.237		

Table 2–7: Local Circumstances for Pennsylvania – West Virginia

Location	Lat °	Long °	First Contact Time h m s	V °	Alt °	Second Contact Time h m s	V °	Third Contact Time h m s	V °	Fourth Contact Time h m s	V °	Alt °	Middle Eclipse Time h m s	V °	Alt °	Azm °	Ecl. Mag.	Ecl. Obs.	FDCL	Durat Total
Pennsylvania																				
Allentown	40.62	−75.48	14:08:10	217	54	–	–	–	–	16:35:03	4	33	15:23:37	286	45	233	0.923	0.915		
Altoona	40.52	−78.40	14:03:26	219	55	–	–	–	–	16:32:13	6	35	15:19:37	288	47	229	0.954	0.953		
Erie	42.13	−80.08	14:02:27	219	54	15:16:21.3	35	15:20:04.7	187	16:30:51	12	36	15:18:15	291	47	225	1.052	1.000	−0.238	03m42s
Harrisburg	40.27	−76.88	14:05:39	218	55	–	–	–	–	16:33:38	4	34	15:21:33	286	46	231	0.929	0.922		
Johnstown	40.32	−78.92	14:02:25	220	56	–	–	–	–	16:31:37	6	36	15:18:46	288	48	228	0.954	0.953		
Lancaster	40.03	−76.32	14:06:23	218	55	–	–	–	–	16:34:06	3	34	15:22:12	286	46	232	0.915	0.905		
Meadville	41.65	−80.15	14:01:50	219	55	15:16:31.9	68	15:19:09.8	153	16:30:41	10	36	15:17:53	290	47	225	1.053	1.000	−0.731	02m37s
Philadelphia	39.95	−75.17	14:08:12	217	54	–	–	–	–	16:35:08	1	33	15:23:43	285	45	234	0.900	0.886		
Pittsburgh	40.43	−80.02	14:00:48	221	56	–	–	–	–	16:30:32	7	37	15:17:19	289	48	226	0.971	0.973		
Reading	40.33	−75.93	14:07:14	217	54	–	–	–	–	16:34:33	3	33	15:22:52	286	45	233	0.920	0.911		
Scranton	41.42	−75.67	14:08:29	216	53	–	–	–	–	16:35:05	6	33	15:23:44	287	44	232	0.949	0.947		
Sharon	41.23	−80.52	14:00:51	220	55	–	–	–	–	16:30:13	10	37	15:17:07	290	48	225	1.000	0.999		
York	39.97	−76.73	14:05:39	218	55	–	–	–	–	16:33:40	3	34	15:21:35	286	46	232	0.918	0.909		
Rhode Island																				
Cranston	41.78	−71.43	14:15:16	213	51	–	–	–	–	16:38:48	4	29	15:29:13	285	41	238	0.918	0.908		
East Providence	41.80	−71.37	14:15:22	213	51	–	–	–	–	16:38:51	5	29	15:29:18	285	41	238	0.917	0.907		
Newport	41.48	−71.32	14:15:18	213	51	–	–	–	–	16:38:51	4	29	15:29:17	285	41	238	0.907	0.895		
Pawtucket	41.88	−71.38	14:15:23	213	51	–	–	–	–	16:38:51	5	29	15:29:18	285	41	238	0.920	0.911		
Providence	41.82	−71.40	14:15:20	213	51	–	–	–	–	16:38:49	5	29	15:29:16	285	41	238	0.918	0.909		
Warwick	41.70	−71.47	14:15:10	213	51	–	–	–	–	16:38:45	4	29	15:29:09	285	41	238	0.915	0.905		
South Carolina																				
Anderson	34.52	−82.65	13:49:57	231	63	–	–	–	–	16:23:49	352	42	15:08:19	284	55	225	0.840	0.810		
Charleston	32.77	−79.93	13:53:39	229	64	–	–	–	–	16:24:57	344	41	15:10:59	279	54	231	0.751	0.697		
Columbia	34.00	−81.05	13:52:31	230	63	–	–	–	–	16:25:07	349	41	15:10:25	282	54	228	0.802	0.762		
Florence	34.20	−79.77	13:55:15	227	62	–	–	–	–	16:26:42	348	40	15:12:42	281	53	231	0.789	0.745		
Greenville	34.85	−82.40	13:50:48	231	62	–	–	–	–	16:24:26	353	42	15:09:05	284	55	225	0.846	0.817		
North Charleston	32.88	−80.00	13:53:37	229	64	–	–	–	–	16:25:01	345	41	15:11:00	279	54	231	0.755	0.702		
Rock Hill	34.93	−81.02	13:53:30	228	62	–	–	–	–	16:26:03	352	41	15:11:23	283	53	228	0.828	0.795		
Spartanburg	34.93	−81.95	13:51:44	230	62	–	–	–	–	16:25:02	353	41	15:09:54	284	54	226	0.842	0.812		
South Dakota																				
Rapid City	44.08	−103.23	11:38:52	230	50	–	–	–	–	13:58:48	53	51	12:48:27	142	53	177	0.655	0.578		
Sioux Falls	43.55	−96.73	12:43:35	229	53	–	–	–	–	15:09:28	38	48	13:56:38	132	54	192	0.767	0.718		
Tennessee																				
Bristol	36.60	−82.18	13:53:06	228	61	–	–	–	–	16:26:07	358	41	15:11:07	286	53	225	0.892	0.875		
Chattanooga	35.05	−85.32	13:45:40	235	63	–	–	–	–	16:21:10	357	45	15:04:34	288	57	219	0.896	0.881		
Clarksville	36.53	−87.35	12:44:12	236	61	–	–	–	–	15:19:49	4	46	14:02:57	293	57	214	0.968	0.970		
Jackson	35.62	−88.82	12:40:27	239	62	–	–	–	–	15:17:10	4	47	13:59:34	294	59	211	0.968	0.970		
Johnson City	36.32	−82.35	13:52:30	228	61	–	–	–	–	16:25:43	357	41	15:10:35	286	53	224	0.886	0.868		
Kingsport	36.55	−82.55	13:52:24	228	61	–	–	–	–	16:25:40	358	41	15:10:30	287	53	224	0.896	0.880		
Knoxville	35.97	−83.92	13:49:18	231	61	–	–	–	–	16:23:39	358	43	15:07:48	288	55	222	0.900	0.885		
Memphis	35.13	−90.05	12:37:43	241	62	–	–	–	–	15:15:05	4	49	13:56:59	296	60	208	0.976	0.979		
Murfreesboro	35.85	−86.40	12:44:50	236	62	–	–	–	–	15:20:30	1	45	14:03:42	291	57	216	0.935	0.930		
Nashville	36.17	−86.78	12:44:37	235	61	–	–	–	–	15:20:17	2	45	14:03:27	292	57	215	0.949	0.948		
Utah																				
Ogden	41.22	−111.97	11:26:41	237	47	–	–	–	–	13:41:06	72	56	12:32:51	158	54	156	0.567	0.473		
Orem	40.32	−111.70	11:24:41	239	47	–	–	–	–	13:41:10	70	57	12:31:50	158	55	155	0.588	0.498		
Provo	40.23	−111.65	11:24:33	240	47	–	–	–	–	13:41:14	69	57	12:31:48	158	55	155	0.589	0.500		
Salt Lake City	40.75	−111.88	11:25:38	238	47	–	–	–	–	13:41:02	71	57	12:32:15	158	55	155	0.576	0.485		
Sandy City	40.60	−111.60	11:25:24	239	47	–	–	–	–	13:41:31	70	57	12:32:23	158	55	156	0.584	0.494		
West Valley	40.68	−111.98	11:25:23	239	47	–	–	–	–	13:40:46	71	57	12:32:00	158	55	155	0.576	0.485		
Vermont																				
Burlington	44.48	−73.20	14:14:16	212	49	15:26:07.8	43	15:29:23.0	175	16:37:21	13	29	15:27:47	289	40	234	1.051	1.000	−0.406	03m15s
Montpelier	44.27	−72.58	14:15:00	212	49	15:27:33.6	81	15:29:17.3	137	16:37:54	12	29	15:28:27	289	40	235	1.051	1.000	−0.882	01m40s
Rutland	43.62	−72.97	14:14:02	213	50	–	–	–	–	16:37:37	11	30	15:27:51	288	41	235	0.987	0.991		
South Burlington	44.45	−73.18	14:14:16	212	49	15:26:11.3	46	15:29:21.7	172	16:37:22	13	29	15:27:47	289	40	234	1.051	1.000	−0.451	03m11s
Virginia																				
Alexandria	38.80	−77.05	14:04:11	220	56	–	–	–	–	16:32:52	360	35	15:20:27	285	47	232	0.888	0.870		
Arlington	38.88	−77.12	14:04:08	220	56	–	–	–	–	16:32:51	360	35	15:20:25	285	47	232	0.891	0.874		
Chesapeake	36.83	−76.28	14:04:04	220	58	–	–	–	–	16:32:28	353	35	15:20:17	282	48	234	0.820	0.785		
Hampton	37.03	−76.35	14:04:05	220	58	–	–	–	–	16:32:32	354	35	15:20:19	282	48	234	0.827	0.793		
Lynchburg	37.42	−79.15	13:59:20	223	59	–	–	–	–	16:29:59	357	37	15:16:26	284	50	229	0.874	0.852		
Newport News	36.98	−76.42	14:03:55	220	58	–	–	–	–	16:32:26	354	35	15:20:11	282	48	234	0.827	0.792		
Norfolk	36.85	−76.28	14:04:04	220	58	–	–	–	–	16:32:28	353	35	15:20:18	282	48	234	0.821	0.785		
Portsmouth	36.83	−76.30	14:04:02	220	58	–	–	–	–	16:32:27	353	35	15:20:16	282	48	234	0.821	0.785		
Richmond	37.55	−77.45	14:02:29	221	58	–	–	–	–	16:31:48	356	36	15:19:04	283	48	232	0.856	0.830		
Roanoke	37.27	−79.93	13:57:48	224	59	–	–	–	–	16:29:04	358	38	15:15:09	285	51	228	0.880	0.860		
Virginia Beach	36.85	−75.98	14:04:38	220	58	–	–	–	–	16:32:46	353	35	15:20:44	281	48	235	0.817	0.781		
Washington																				
Bellevue	47.62	−122.20	10:39:03	220	39	–	–	–	–	12:21:35	108	49	11:29:32	165	45	144	0.312	0.202		
Bellingham	48.77	−122.48	10:41:55	217	38	–	–	–	–	12:21:17	109	48	11:30:53	165	44	144	0.293	0.184		
Everett	47.98	−122.20	10:39:58	219	39	–	–	–	–	12:21:42	108	48	11:30:05	165	44	144	0.307	0.197		
Olympia	47.05	−122.88	10:37:35	221	38	–	–	–	–	12:19:53	109	49	11:27:56	167	45	142	0.310	0.200		
Pasco	46.23	−119.10	10:36:02	224	41	–	–	–	–	12:27:56	98	51	11:31:07	163	47	147	0.375	0.264		
Seattle	47.60	−122.33	10:39:01	220	39	–	–	–	–	12:21:17	108	49	11:29:22	165	45	143	0.310	0.200		
Spokane	47.67	−117.40	10:39:54	222	41	–	–	–	–	12:31:55	95	50	11:35:09	160	47	152	0.378	0.267		
Tacoma	47.23	−122.43	10:38:05	221	39	–	–	–	–	12:20:57	108	49	11:28:43	166	45	143	0.314	0.204		
Yakima	46.60	−120.52	10:36:42	223	40	–	–	–	–	12:24:58	102	50	11:30:00	164	46	145	0.349	0.238		
West Virginia																				
Charleston	38.35	−81.63	13:55:59	225	59	–	–	–	–	16:27:52	2	39	15:13:28	288	51	224	0.933	0.928		
Huntington	38.42	−82.45	13:54:42	226	59	–	–	–	–	16:26:59	4	40	15:12:19	289	52	223	0.946	0.944		
Parkersburg	39.27	−81.57	13:57:05	224	58	–	–	–	–	16:28:23	5	39	15:14:17	289	50	224	0.958	0.958		
Wheeling	40.07	−80.72	13:59:19	222	57	–	–	–	–	16:29:39	6	38	15:16:05	289	49	225	0.969	0.972		

Table 2–8: Local Circumstances for Texas, Wisconsin & Wyoming

Location	Lat	Long	First Contact Time	First Contact V	First Contact Alt	Second Contact Time	Second Contact V	Third Contact Time	Third Contact V	Fourth Contact Time	Fourth Contact V	Fourth Contact Alt	Middle Eclipse Time	Middle Eclipse V	Middle Eclipse Alt	Middle Eclipse Azm	Ecl. Mag.	Ecl. Obs.	FDCL	Durat Total
	°	°	h m s	°	°	h m s	°	h m s	°	h m s	°	°	h m s	°	°	°				
Texas																				
Allen	33.10	-96.67	12:24:06	254	60	13:41:41.1	1	13:44:59.6	259	15:03:15	12	56	13:43:22	130	64	189	1.056	1.000	0.646	03m19s
Amarillo	35.22	-101.83	12:21:43	251	56	-	-	-	-	14:56:39	30	58	13:38:26	142	62	174	0.865	0.842		
Arlington	32.73	-97.12	12:22:46	256	60	13:40:23.1	2	13:43:41.5	261	15:02:08	12	57	13:42:04	131	65	187	1.056	1.000	0.649	03m19s
Austin	30.28	-97.75	12:17:15	263	61	13:35:59.4	110	13:37:59.0	158	14:58:09	7	60	13:37:04	314	67	183	1.056	1.000	-0.906	01m52s
Beaumont	30.08	-94.10	12:22:42	260	64	-	-	-	-	15:03:31	358	57	13:42:56	303	67	196	0.926	0.919		
Bedford	32.85	-97.13	12:22:58	255	60	13:40:46.1	353	13:43:39.4	270	15:02:14	12	57	13:42:13	131	65	187	1.056	1.000	0.756	02m51s
Benbrook	32.68	-97.47	12:22:11	256	60	13:40:13.7	345	13:42:35.1	280	15:01:31	13	57	13:41:25	132	65	186	1.056	1.000	0.848	02m19s
Brownsville	25.90	-97.50	12:09:34	277	63	-	-	-	-	14:51:50	355	64	13:29:46	317	72	179	0.898	0.884		
Burleson	32.55	-97.32	12:22:08	256	60	13:39:44.9	3	13:43:06.1	260	15:01:36	12	57	13:41:27	132	65	186	1.056	1.000	0.635	03m22s
Carrollton	32.95	-96.92	12:23:28	255	60	13:41:07.5	358	13:44:17.3	264	15:02:41	12	57	13:42:43	131	64	188	1.056	1.000	0.691	03m09s
Cedar Hill	32.58	-96.97	12:22:42	256	61	13:40:05.0	17	13:43:59.7	245	15:02:12	11	57	13:42:04	131	65	187	1.056	1.000	0.422	03m58s
Cleburne	32.35	-97.38	12:21:40	257	60	13:39:08.3	12	13:42:50.8	252	15:01:16	12	58	13:41:01	132	65	186	1.056	1.000	0.517	03m45s
Colleyville	32.88	-97.15	12:23:00	255	60	13:40:53.3	349	13:43:34.8	273	15:02:15	12	57	13:42:14	131	65	187	1.056	1.000	0.795	02m39s
Coppell	32.95	-97.02	12:23:19	255	60	13:41:07.3	352	13:43:59.7	270	15:02:32	12	57	13:42:33	131	64	187	1.056	1.000	0.759	02m50s
Copperas Cove	31.13	-97.90	12:18:38	261	61	13:36:00.8	52	13:40:22.9	216	14:58:59	10	59	13:38:13	314	66	183	1.056	1.000	-0.115	04m23s
Corpus Christi	27.78	-97.40	12:13:09	271	63	-	-	-	-	14:55:05	360	62	13:33:21	315	70	182	0.939	0.935		
Corsicana	32.10	-96.47	12:22:32	257	61	13:40:01.2	59	13:44:12.2	200	15:02:27	9	57	13:42:08	310	65	189	1.056	1.000	-0.321	04m09s
Dallas	32.78	-96.82	12:23:18	255	61	13:40:42.6	12	13:44:28.9	249	15:02:40	11	57	13:42:38	130	65	188	1.056	1.000	0.486	03m49s
Del Rio	29.37	-100.90	12:10:59	268	59	13:28:31.1	16	13:31:54.0	274	14:51:39	14	63	13:30:14	145	68	170	1.056	1.000	0.641	03m24s
Denton	33.22	-97.13	12:23:39	254	60	-	-	-	-	15:02:38	13	57	13:42:47	131	64	187	0.998	1.000		
Duncanville	32.65	-96.92	12:22:54	256	61	13:40:17.1	15	13:44:09.4	246	15:02:22	11	57	13:42:15	131	65	188	1.056	1.000	0.443	03m55s
Eagle Pass	28.72	-100.50	12:10:15	270	59	13:27:32.1	65	13:31:55.3	224	14:51:25	11	64	13:29:45	324	69	171	1.056	1.000	-0.155	04m24s
El Paso	31.75	-106.48	11:09:23	262	53	-	-	-	-	13:44:30	38	64	12:25:30	157	64	156	0.846	0.818		
Euless	32.83	-97.08	12:23:00	255	60	13:40:42.4	357	13:43:48.4	266	15:02:18	12	57	13:42:16	131	65	187	1.056	1.000	0.709	03m05s
Farmers Branch	32.93	-96.90	12:23:27	255	60	13:41:04.8	360	13:44:19.7	262	15:02:42	12	57	13:42:43	131	64	188	1.056	1.000	0.666	03m15s
Flower Mound	33.03	-97.15	12:23:17	255	60	13:41:36.1	335	13:43:16.6	288	15:02:24	13	57	13:42:28	131	64	187	1.056	1.000	0.919	01m43s
Fort Worth	32.75	-97.30	12:22:33	256	60	13:40:25.6	350	13:43:09.0	273	15:01:52	12	57	13:41:47	132	65	186	1.056	1.000	0.790	02m40s
Frisco	33.15	-96.82	12:23:59	254	60	13:41:49.8	349	13:44:33.0	272	15:03:04	12	56	13:43:11	130	64	188	1.056	1.000	0.789	02m40s
Galveston	29.30	-94.80	12:20:09	264	64	-	-	-	-	15:01:22	358	58	13:40:26	305	68	193	0.921	0.913		
Garland	32.92	-96.63	12:23:48	255	61	13:41:11.5	13	13:45:00.0	247	15:03:06	11	56	13:43:08	130	64	189	1.056	1.000	0.471	03m51s
Georgetown	30.63	-97.68	12:18:00	262	61	13:36:06.1	87	13:39:22.3	180	14:58:42	8	59	13:37:45	314	67	183	1.056	1.000	-0.672	03m16s
Grand Prairie	32.75	-97.00	12:22:58	256	60	13:40:29.8	6	13:44:00.4	256	15:02:20	12	57	13:42:17	131	65	187	1.056	1.000	0.583	03m33s
Grapevine	32.98	-97.03	12:23:21	255	60	13:41:14.5	349	13:43:54.9	273	15:02:32	12	57	13:42:35	131	64	187	1.056	1.000	0.798	02m37s
Greenville	33.13	-96.12	12:24:57	254	61	13:42:14.4	22	13:46:20.7	235	15:04:10	11	56	13:44:19	129	64	190	1.056	1.000	0.301	04m09s
Haltom City	32.80	-97.27	12:22:41	256	60	13:40:35.9	349	13:43:13.6	275	15:01:58	13	57	13:41:55	132	65	187	1.056	1.000	0.806	02m35s
Houston	29.77	-95.37	12:20:02	263	63	-	-	-	-	15:01:11	0	58	13:40:14	307	67	191	0.943	0.940		
Hurst	32.82	-97.15	12:22:53	255	60	13:40:39.0	354	13:43:36.6	268	15:02:10	12	57	13:42:08	131	65	187	1.056	1.000	0.740	02m56s
Irving	32.82	-96.93	12:23:11	255	60	13:40:43.5	5	13:44:12.2	256	15:02:31	12	57	13:42:29	131	65	188	1.056	1.000	0.592	03m31s
Keller	32.93	-97.25	12:22:57	255	60	13:41:12.2	337	13:43:04.1	286	15:02:08	13	57	13:42:09	132	65	187	1.056	1.000	0.905	01m51s
Kerrville	30.05	-99.13	12:14:47	265	60	13:32:08.2	56	13:36:32.0	221	14:55:34	10	61	13:34:21	319	68	178	1.056	1.000	-0.104	04m24s
Killeen	31.12	-97.73	12:18:50	261	61	13:36:17.6	59	13:40:34.6	208	14:59:14	9	59	13:38:28	314	66	184	1.056	1.000	-0.245	04m16s
Lancaster	32.58	-96.75	12:23:01	256	61	13:40:19.9	25	13:44:29.6	235	15:02:33	11	57	13:42:26	130	65	188	1.056	1.000	0.274	04m12s
Laredo	27.50	-99.50	12:09:21	273	61	-	-	-	-	14:51:17	5	64	13:29:15	323	70	172	0.976	0.980		
Lewisville	33.05	-97.00	12:23:32	255	60	13:41:30.1	345	13:43:58.0	277	15:02:40	13	57	13:42:44	131	64	188	1.056	1.000	0.831	02m25s
Lubbock	33.58	-101.85	12:18:19	256	57	-	-	-	-	14:55:04	27	60	13:35:50	143	64	173	0.900	0.886		
Mansfield	32.57	-97.15	12:22:25	256	60	13:39:53.4	10	13:43:32.9	253	15:01:54	12	57	13:41:45	131	65	187	1.056	1.000	0.534	03m42s
McAllen	26.20	-98.23	12:08:54	277	62	-	-	-	-	14:51:12	358	64	13:29:03	319	71	176	0.920	0.912		
McKinney	33.20	-96.62	12:24:21	254	60	13:42:00.5	357	13:45:09.2	263	15:03:26	12	56	13:43:36	130	64	189	1.056	1.000	0.695	03m08s
Mesquite	32.77	-96.60	12:23:34	255	61	13:40:54.0	22	13:44:58.8	238	15:03:00	11	57	13:42:57	130	65	189	1.056	1.000	0.323	04m08s
North Richland H	32.83	-97.23	12:22:48	255	60	13:40:43.1	348	13:43:19.1	275	15:02:03	13	57	13:42:01	132	65	187	1.056	1.000	0.811	02m33s
Paris	33.67	-95.55	12:26:45	252	61	13:44:01.2	16	13:47:59.5	238	15:05:36	11	55	13:46:02	127	63	192	1.056	1.000	0.370	04m02s
Pasadena	29.72	-95.22	12:20:11	263	63	-	-	-	-	15:01:20	360	58	13:40:25	306	67	192	0.939	0.935		
Plano	33.02	-96.70	12:23:54	255	61	13:41:25.6	4	13:44:52.8	256	15:03:07	12	56	13:43:11	130	64	188	1.056	1.000	0.599	03m29s
Richardson	32.95	-96.73	12:23:43	255	61	13:41:13.2	7	13:44:46.4	254	15:02:59	12	57	13:43:01	130	64	188	1.056	1.000	0.566	03m35s
Round Rock	30.52	-97.68	12:17:47	263	61	13:36:06.4	95	13:38:58.8	173	14:58:33	8	59	13:37:33	314	67	183	1.056	1.000	-0.767	02m50s
Rowlett	32.90	-96.57	12:23:52	255	61	13:41:13.5	16	13:45:08.8	243	15:03:12	11	56	13:43:13	130	64	189	1.056	1.000	0.412	03m58s
San Antonio	29.42	-98.50	12:14:29	267	61	-	-	-	-	14:55:45	7	61	13:34:20	317	68	179	0.998	0.999		
Sherman	33.63	-96.60	12:25:11	253	60	-	-	-	-	15:03:55	13	56	13:44:17	130	64	189	0.999	1.000		
Temple	31.10	-97.35	12:19:22	261	61	13:37:10.2	75	13:40:57.7	190	14:59:50	8	59	13:39:04	312	66	185	1.056	1.000	-0.529	03m45s
Texarkana	33.43	-94.05	12:28:35	251	62	13:46:51.3	90	13:49:22.2	157	15:07:40	7	54	13:48:09	304	63	197	1.056	1.000	-0.827	02m26s
The Colony	33.08	-96.88	12:23:45	254	60	13:41:35.6	350	13:44:22.2	271	15:02:53	12	57	13:42:59	131	64	188	1.056	1.000	0.779	02m44s
Tyler	32.35	-95.30	12:24:45	255	62	13:43:25.9	103	13:45:21.0	150	15:04:34	7	56	13:44:28	307	65	193	1.056	1.000	-0.911	01m48s
University Park	32.85	-96.80	12:23:26	255	61	13:40:53.9	9	13:44:33.8	251	15:02:46	12	57	13:42:45	130	65	188	1.056	1.000	0.529	03m42s
Uvalde	29.22	-99.78	12:12:14	268	60	13:29:39.7	70	13:33:56.5	213	14:53:20	10	62	13:31:50	321	68	174	1.056	1.000	-0.290	04m15s
Waco	31.55	-97.15	12:20:30	259	61	13:37:59.7	60	13:42:13.3	203	15:00:43	9	58	13:40:08	312	66	186	1.056	1.000	-0.300	04m12s
Watauga	32.87	-97.27	12:22:49	255	60	13:40:53.5	343	13:43:08.8	281	15:02:02	13	57	13:42:01	132	65	187	1.056	1.000	0.861	02m13s
Waxahachie	32.40	-96.85	12:22:32	256	61	13:39:49.1	31	13:44:06.0	231	15:02:11	11	57	13:41:59	131	65	188	1.056	1.000	0.191	04m18s
Wisconsin																				
Appleton	44.27	-88.42	12:54:00	222	53	-	-	-	-	15:21:19	27	42	14:08:30	121	50	209	0.869	0.847		
Eau Claire	44.82	-91.50	12:51:19	223	53	-	-	-	-	15:17:13	33	43	14:04:50	125	51	203	0.813	0.776		
Green Bay	44.52	-88.00	12:54:52	222	53	-	-	-	-	15:21:51	27	41	14:09:14	121	50	210	0.868	0.846		
Kenosha	42.58	-87.82	12:52:15	225	55	-	-	-	-	15:21:56	22	42	14:08:01	119	51	211	0.921	0.912		
La Crosse	43.80	-91.25	12:49:56	225	54	-	-	-	-	15:17:31	30	44	14:04:20	124	52	203	0.842	0.812		
Madison	43.07	-89.40	12:50:59	225	54	-	-	-	-	15:19:57	25	43	14:06:14	121	52	207	0.886	0.869		
Milwaukee	43.03	-87.92	12:52:48	224	55	-	-	-	-	15:21:53	23	42	14:08:14	119	51	210	0.908	0.896		
Racine	42.73	-87.80	12:52:30	224	55	-	-	-	-	15:21:59	22	42	14:08:10	119	51	211	0.917	0.908		
Sheboygan	43.77	-87.75	12:54:04	223	54	-	-	-	-	15:22:09	25	41	14:09:01	120	50	210	0.891	0.874		
Wyoming																				
Casper	42.85	-106.32	11:33:54	233	49	-	-	-	-	13:52:51	58	53	12:42:45	147	54	170	0.631	0.549		
Cheyenne	41.13	-104.82	11:31:23	237	51	-	-	-	-	13:55:04	51	54	12:42:35	145	56	172	0.688	0.619		
Laramie	41.32	-105.58	11:31:07	237	50	-	-	-	-	13:53:40	53	55	12:41:43	147	56	170	0.673	0.600		

Table 2–9: Local Circumstances for Canada (Alberta – Saskatchewan)

Location	Lat °	Long °	First Contact Time h m s	V °	Alt °	Second Contact Time h m s	V °	Third Contact Time h m s	V °	Fourth Contact Time h m s	V °	Alt °	Middle Eclipse Time h m s	V °	Alt °	Azm °	Ecl. Mag.	Ecl. Obs.	FDCL	Durat Total
Alberta																				
Calgary	51.05	-114.08	11:48:38	215	41	–	–	–	–	13:38:53	91	47	12:43:14	154	45	161	0.373	0.262		
Edmonton	53.55	-113.47	11:54:24	210	40	–	–	–	–	13:39:44	93	44	12:46:40	152	43	163	0.344	0.232		
Lethbridge	49.70	-112.83	11:45:54	218	42	–	–	–	–	13:41:21	86	48	12:43:04	153	47	162	0.411	0.301		
Medicine Hat	50.05	-110.67	11:47:27	218	43	–	–	–	–	13:45:27	82	47	12:45:58	151	47	166	0.436	0.326		
Red Deer	52.27	-113.80	11:51:26	213	40	–	–	–	–	13:39:19	92	45	12:44:55	153	44	162	0.359	0.247		
British Columbia																				
Abbotsford	49.05	-122.28	10:42:38	217	38	–	–	–	–	12:21:47	109	47	11:31:31	164	44	145	0.292	0.184		
Kamloops	50.67	-120.33	10:46:42	214	39	–	–	–	–	12:26:15	106	46	11:35:52	161	43	150	0.297	0.188		
Kelowna	49.88	-119.48	10:44:52	216	39	–	–	–	–	12:27:56	103	47	11:35:45	161	44	150	0.319	0.208		
Matsqui	49.20	-122.42	10:43:00	217	38	–	–	–	–	12:21:32	109	47	11:31:35	164	43	145	0.289	0.180		
Nanaimo	49.17	-123.93	10:42:55	216	37	–	–	–	–	12:18:12	113	47	11:29:53	166	43	142	0.269	0.163		
Prince George	53.92	-122.75	10:54:37	207	36	–	–	–	–	12:21:27	114	43	11:37:35	161	40	149	0.227	0.127		
Richmond	49.17	-123.17	10:42:54	216	38	–	–	–	–	12:19:53	111	47	11:30:43	165	43	144	0.279	0.172		
Vancouver	49.27	-123.12	10:43:09	216	38	–	–	–	–	12:20:01	111	47	11:30:55	165	43	144	0.278	0.171		
Victoria	48.42	-123.37	13:41:01	218	38	–	–	–	–	15:19:15	111	48	14:29:25	166	43	143	0.286	0.178		
Manitoba																				
Winnipeg	49.88	-97.15	12:54:52	217	47	–	–	–	–	15:08:13	55	43	14:01:42	135	47	192	0.620	0.536		
New Brunswick																				
Blackville	46.74	-65.83	15:24:58	207	43	16:34:02.3	19	16:37:19.4	200	17:42:10	16	23	16:35:42	109	34	242	1.049	1.000	0.005	03m18s
Bathurst	47.62	-65.65	15:25:28	207	42	–	–	–	–	17:41:54	19	23	16:35:46	110	33	241	0.998	0.999		
Dieppe	46.10	-64.72	15:26:10	207	43	–	–	–	–	17:43:05	14	22	16:36:49	288	33	243	0.998	0.999		
Doaktown	46.55	-66.13	15:24:32	207	44	16:33:44.8	28	16:37:03.7	191	17:42:03	16	23	16:35:25	289	34	241	1.049	1.000	-0.144	03m16s
Fredericton	45.96	-66.64	15:23:43	208	44	16:33:47.0	66	16:36:05.7	151	17:41:55	14	24	16:34:58	289	35	241	1.049	1.000	-0.733	02m16s
Grand Falls	47.03	-67.74	15:22:45	208	44	16:33:04.6	316	16:34:24.0	265	17:40:49	18	24	16:33:50	110	35	239	1.049	1.000	0.902	01m27s
Hartland	46.30	-67.53	15:22:43	208	45	16:32:22.4	23	16:35:44.4	196	17:41:13	16	24	16:34:04	289	35	240	1.050	1.000	-0.062	03m21s
Miramichi	47.02	-65.51	15:25:27	207	43	16:34:23.3	3	16:37:29.4	216	17:42:15	17	23	16:35:58	110	33	242	1.049	1.000	0.282	03m09s
Moncton	46.13	-64.77	15:26:07	207	43	–	–	–	–	17:43:03	14	22	16:36:46	288	33	243	0.999	1.000		
Nackawic	46.00	-67.24	15:22:58	208	45	16:32:56.6	50	16:35:47.8	167	17:41:31	15	24	16:34:23	289	35	240	1.049	1.000	-0.521	02m52s
Neguac	47.23	-65.05	15:26:03	207	42	16:34:53.6	355	16:37:48.4	225	17:42:27	17	22	16:36:22	110	33	242	1.049	1.000	0.429	02m57s
Perth-Andover	46.75	-67.70	15:22:41	208	44	16:32:28.0	347	16:35:16.3	232	17:40:57	17	24	16:33:53	110	35	239	1.049	1.000	0.540	02m49s
Rogersville	46.72	-65.42	15:25:28	207	43	16:34:25.4	27	16:37:43.4	192	17:42:26	16	23	16:36:06	289	33	242	1.049	1.000	-0.127	03m15s
St. Louis de Ken	46.73	-64.97	15:26:01	207	43	16:34:52.8	32	16:38:05.8	186	17:42:42	16	22	16:36:31	289	33	243	1.049	1.000	-0.223	03m11s
Saint John	45.28	-66.08	15:24:14	208	44	–	–	–	–	17:42:29	12	24	16:35:34	288	34	242	0.982	0.985		
Shippagan	47.74	-64.72	15:26:35	206	42	16:36:21.6	299	16:36:41.9	282	17:42:25	19	22	16:36:35	110	32	242	1.049	1.000	0.988	00m30s
Tracadie-Sheila	47.51	-64.92	15:26:18	206	42	16:35:21.3	332	16:37:31.9	248	17:42:24	18	22	16:36:27	110	33	242	1.049	1.000	0.749	02m09s
Woodstock	46.15	-67.57	15:22:36	208	45	16:32:21.8	33	16:35:38.9	185	17:41:15	15	25	16:34:02	289	35	240	1.050	1.000	-0.239	03m16s
Newfoundland																				
Buchans	48.83	-56.86	15:05:15	204	36	16:11:42.7	327	16:13:29.1	254	17:15:43	20	16	16:12:37	110	26	250	1.047	1.000	0.807	01m46s
Channel Port Aux	47.57	-59.14	15:02:52	205	38	16:09:59.3	46	16:12:42.8	172	17:15:26	17	18	16:11:22	289	28	249	1.048	1.000	-0.455	02m45s
Clarenville	48.16	-53.97	15:08:11	204	34	16:13:37.8	50	16:16:08.0	168	17:17:11	18	14	16:14:53	289	24	253	1.046	1.000	-0.512	02m31s
Corner Brook	48.95	-54.95	15:07:07	203	35	16:12:48.9	336	16:14:57.5	244	17:16:22	20	15	16:13:53	110	25	252	1.047	1.000	0.694	02m07s
Gander	48.96	-54.61	15:07:27	203	34	16:12:59.2	339	16:15:13.6	241	17:16:29	20	15	16:14:07	110	25	252	1.047	1.000	0.657	02m13s
Grand Falls-Wind	48.94	-55.65	15:06:27	204	35	16:12:28.0	330	16:14:21.9	251	17:16:07	20	15	16:13:25	110	25	251	1.047	1.000	0.773	01m53s
Mount Pearl	47.52	-52.81	15:09:27	204	34	–	–	–	–	17:17:55	16	13	16:15:56	289	24	255	0.988	0.991		
Paradise	47.53	-52.87	15:09:23	204	34	–	–	–	–	17:17:53	16	13	16:15:53	289	24	255	0.988	0.992		
Port Rexton	48.40	-53.32	15:08:46	204	34	16:13:45.8	35	16:16:35.0	184	17:17:15	19	14	16:15:12	290	24	254	1.046	1.000	-0.266	02m48s
Saint John's	47.56	-52.71	15:09:32	204	34	–	–	–	–	17:17:55	16	13	16:15:58	289	23	255	0.989	0.992		
Stephenville	48.55	-58.57	15:03:30	204	37	16:10:25.1	333	16:12:31.6	247	17:15:09	20	17	16:11:28	110	28	249	1.047	1.000	0.729	02m05s
Northwest Territories																				
Aklavik	68.20	-135.00	12:38:31	167	25	–	–	–	–	12:52:22	154	26	12:45:28	161	25	142	0.006	0.001		
Fort Simpson	61.87	-121.38	12:12:52	193	32	–	–	–	–	13:23:04	119	35	12:47:47	156	34	156	0.154	0.072		
Inuvik	68.42	-133.50	12:35:50	171	25	–	–	–	–	12:57:14	149	26	12:46:32	160	26	144	0.015	0.002		
Yellowknife	62.45	-114.35	12:13:25	194	33	–	–	–	–	13:34:44	108	35	12:53:55	151	35	166	0.212	0.115		
Nova Scotia																				
Halifax	44.65	-63.60	15:27:19	208	43	–	–	–	–	17:44:08	10	22	16:38:03	286	33	245	0.946	0.943		
Sydney	46.15	-60.18	15:31:40	206	40	–	–	–	–	17:45:33	13	19	16:40:54	288	30	248	0.974	0.976		
Prince Edward Island																				
Alberton	46.82	-64.07	15:27:08	207	42	16:35:47.5	39	16:38:49.8	179	17:43:12	16	22	16:37:20	289	32	244	1.049	1.000	-0.345	03m03s
Charlottetown	46.23	-63.13	15:28:09	207	42	–	–	–	–	17:43:58	14	21	16:38:17	288	32	245	0.992	0.995		
Kennsington	46.43	-63.65	15:27:33	207	42	16:37:08.4	88	16:38:21.9	129	17:43:36	15	21	16:37:47	288	32	244	1.049	1.000	-0.935	01m09s
O'Leary	46.71	-64.23	15:26:54	207	42	16:35:44.6	45	16:38:38.3	172	17:43:09	16	22	16:37:12	289	32	244	1.049	1.000	-0.443	02m55s
North Rustico	46.48	-63.38	15:27:53	207	42	16:37:22.9	88	16:38:35.2	129	17:43:44	15	21	16:38:01	288	32	245	1.049	1.000	-0.938	01m07s
Summerside	46.40	-63.78	15:27:23	207	42	16:37:03.0	89	16:38:11.9	127	17:43:32	15	22	16:37:40	288	32	244	1.049	1.000	-0.945	01m04s
Tignish	46.95	-64.03	15:27:12	207	42	16:35:42.8	30	16:38:56.1	188	17:43:10	16	22	16:37:21	289	32	244	1.049	1.000	-0.183	03m11s
Saskatchewan																				
Regina	50.42	-104.65	11:51:03	217	45	–	–	–	–	13:56:09	70	46	12:53:21	143	47	177	0.510	0.408		
Saskatoon	52.12	-106.63	11:53:35	214	43	–	–	–	–	13:52:19	77	45	12:52:40	146	45	175	0.453	0.345		

Table 2–10: Local Circumstances for Canada (Ontario & Québec)

Location	Lat °	Long °	First Contact Time h m s	V °	Alt °	Second Contact Time h m s	V °	Third Contact Time h m s	V °	Fourth Contact Time h m s	V °	Alt °	Middle Eclipse Time h m s	V °	Alt °	Azm °	Ecl. Mag.	Ecl. Obs.	FDCL	Durat Total
Ontario																				
Barrie	44.40	-79.67	14:05:22	216	52	–	–	–	–	16:31:22	18	35	15:19:55	113	45	224	0.973	0.976		
Brampton	43.68	-79.77	14:04:29	217	53	–	–	–	–	16:31:17	16	35	15:19:28	112	46	225	0.992	0.995		
Brantford	43.13	-80.27	14:03:13	218	53	15:17:47.9	315	15:19:05.3	270	16:30:46	15	36	15:18:33	112	46	224	1.052	1.000	0.924	01m27s
Burlington	43.32	-79.78	14:04:05	217	53	15:18:26.9	317	15:19:55.3	267	16:31:16	15	35	15:19:16	112	46	225	1.052	1.000	0.908	01m35s
Cambridge (Galt)	43.37	-80.32	14:03:24	218	53	–	–	–	–	16:30:43	15	36	15:18:36	112	46	224	0.995	0.997		
Cornwall	45.03	-74.73	14:12:35	212	49	15:24:59.8	328	15:27:13.0	253	16:35:58	16	30	15:26:07	111	41	231	1.051	1.000	0.794	02m11s
East York	43.68	-79.33	14:05:05	217	53	–	–	–	–	16:31:44	16	35	15:20:01	112	45	225	0.997	0.999		
Etobicoke	43.65	-79.57	14:04:44	217	53	–	–	–	–	16:31:30	16	35	15:19:42	112	45	225	0.995	0.998		
Gloucester	45.37	-75.58	14:11:42	212	49	–	–	–	–	16:35:09	17	31	15:25:12	112	42	230	0.987	0.991		
Guelph	43.55	-80.25	14:03:42	217	53	–	–	–	–	16:30:48	16	36	15:18:48	113	46	224	0.990	0.994		
Hamilton	43.25	-79.85	14:03:56	217	53	15:18:10.5	322	15:20:03.9	262	16:31:12	15	35	15:19:09	112	46	225	1.052	1.000	0.866	01m53s
Kingston	44.23	-76.50	14:09:32	214	51	15:22:14.6	347	15:25:16.1	235	16:34:28	15	32	15:23:47	111	43	229	1.052	1.000	0.559	03m02s
Kitchener	43.45	-80.48	14:03:16	218	53	–	–	–	–	16:30:34	16	36	15:18:26	113	46	224	0.991	0.994		
London	42.98	-81.23	14:01:42	219	54	–	–	–	–	16:29:44	15	37	15:17:12	113	47	223	0.995	0.997		
Markham	43.87	-79.27	14:05:22	216	52	–	–	–	–	16:31:48	16	35	15:20:11	112	45	225	0.993	0.996		
Mississauga	43.58	-79.62	14:04:36	217	53	–	–	–	–	16:31:27	15	35	15:19:37	112	46	225	0.997	0.999		
Nepean	45.30	-75.78	14:11:23	213	50	–	–	–	–	16:34:59	17	31	15:24:57	112	42	230	0.987	0.991		
Niagara Falls	43.10	-79.07	14:04:53	217	53	15:18:20.5	0	15:21:47.2	222	16:32:00	14	35	15:20:06	111	46	226	1.052	1.000	0.362	03m30s
North Bay	46.32	-79.47	14:07:37	214	50	–	–	–	–	16:31:17	23	34	15:20:56	115	43	224	0.921	0.912		
North York	43.77	-79.42	14:05:03	216	52	–	–	–	–	16:31:39	16	35	15:19:57	112	45	225	0.994	0.997		
Oakville	43.45	-79.68	14:04:22	217	53	–	–	–	–	16:31:22	15	35	15:19:28	112	46	225	1.000	1.000		
Oshawa	43.90	-78.85	14:05:59	216	52	–	–	–	–	16:32:13	16	34	15:20:44	112	45	226	0.996	0.998		
Ottawa	45.42	-75.70	14:11:36	213	49	–	–	–	–	16:35:02	18	31	15:25:05	112	42	230	0.985	0.988		
Peterborough	44.30	-78.32	14:07:06	215	52	–	–	–	–	16:32:44	16	34	15:21:34	112	44	226	0.990	0.994		
Saint Catharines	43.17	-79.25	14:04:42	217	53	15:18:15.8	351	15:21:27.6	232	16:31:49	14	35	15:19:53	111	46	226	1.052	1.000	0.514	03m13s
Sarnia	42.97	-82.38	14:00:04	220	54	–	–	–	–	16:28:28	16	38	15:15:40	114	48	221	0.981	0.985		
Sault Sainte Mar	46.52	-84.33	14:01:58	216	51	–	–	–	–	16:26:01	28	37	15:15:07	119	46	216	0.861	0.837		
Scarborough	43.73	-79.27	14:05:14	216	52	–	–	–	–	16:31:48	16	35	15:20:08	112	45	225	0.996	0.998		
Sudbury	46.50	-81.00	14:05:55	214	50	–	–	–	–	16:29:40	25	35	15:19:10	116	44	221	0.899	0.885		
Thunder Bay	48.38	-89.25	13:59:16	216	49	–	–	–	–	16:19:35	39	40	15:10:09	125	47	206	0.755	0.701		
Toronto	43.65	-79.38	14:04:59	217	53	–	–	–	–	16:31:41	15	35	15:19:57	112	45	225	0.997	0.999		
Waterloo	43.47	-80.52	14:03:13	218	53	–	–	–	–	16:30:30	16	36	15:18:23	113	46	224	0.990	0.993		
Windsor	42.30	-83.02	13:58:24	221	55	–	–	–	–	16:27:41	15	38	15:14:24	114	49	220	0.992	0.995		
York	43.68	-79.48	14:04:53	217	53	–	–	–	–	16:31:35	16	35	15:19:50	112	45	225	0.995	0.998		
Québec																				
Beauport	46.87	-71.18	14:18:25	209	46	–	–	–	–	16:38:23	19	27	15:30:19	111	37	235	0.982	0.985		
Brossard	45.43	-73.48	14:14:32	211	49	15:26:33.7	327	15:28:42.2	254	16:36:57	16	29	15:27:38	111	40	233	1.051	1.000	0.805	02m06s
Charlesbourg	46.85	-71.27	14:18:18	209	46	–	–	–	–	16:38:20	19	27	15:30:14	111	38	235	0.982	0.985		
Chicoutimi	48.43	-71.07	14:19:29	208	45	–	–	–	–	16:37:48	23	27	15:30:28	113	36	234	0.936	0.931		
Drummondville	45.88	-72.48	14:16:09	210	48	15:28:33.1	300	15:28:55.4	281	16:37:40	17	28	15:28:50	111	39	234	1.051	1.000	0.986	00m35s
Gatineau	45.48	-75.63	14:11:44	212	49	–	–	–	–	16:35:05	18	31	15:25:11	112	41	230	0.984	0.987		
Hull	45.43	-75.72	14:11:35	213	49	–	–	–	–	16:35:01	18	31	15:25:04	112	42	230	0.984	0.988		
La Salle	45.43	-73.63	14:14:20	211	49	15:26:32.0	322	15:28:20.6	260	16:36:50	16	29	15:27:28	111	40	233	1.051	1.000	0.858	01m49s
Laval	45.58	-73.75	14:14:17	211	48	–	–	–	–	16:36:42	17	30	15:27:22	111	40	232	0.998	0.999		
Longueuil	45.53	-73.50	14:14:35	211	48	15:26:56.9	313	15:28:05.9	269	16:36:55	16	29	15:27:38	111	40	233	1.051	1.000	0.927	01m19s
Montreal	45.52	-73.57	14:14:29	211	48	15:26:53.5	312	15:27:59.6	269	16:36:52	16	29	15:27:34	111	40	233	1.051	1.000	0.932	01m17s
Montreal Nord	45.60	-73.63	14:14:27	211	48	–	–	–	–	16:36:48	17	29	15:27:30	111	40	232	0.999	1.000		
Quebec	46.82	-71.23	14:18:19	209	46	–	–	–	–	16:38:22	19	27	15:30:16	111	38	235	0.983	0.986		
Sainte Foy	46.78	-71.28	14:18:14	209	46	–	–	–	–	16:38:21	19	27	15:30:13	111	38	235	0.983	0.987		
Saint Hubert	45.50	-73.42	14:14:40	211	48	15:26:47.8	322	15:28:35.7	260	16:37:00	16	29	15:27:44	111	40	233	1.051	1.000	0.859	01m49s
Saint Laurent	45.50	-73.67	14:14:20	211	49	15:26:50.6	310	15:27:46.5	272	16:36:47	17	29	15:27:27	111	40	233	1.051	1.000	0.948	01m08s
Saint Leonard	45.58	-73.58	14:14:30	211	48	–	–	–	–	16:36:50	17	29	15:27:33	111	40	233	1.000	1.000		
Shawinigan	46.55	-72.75	14:16:15	210	47	–	–	–	–	16:37:16	19	28	15:28:37	112	39	233	0.978	0.981		
Sherbrooke	45.40	-71.90	14:16:37	211	48	15:27:42.3	7	15:31:04.6	212	16:38:16	15	28	15:29:25	110	39	235	1.050	1.000	0.219	03m25s
Trois Riviares	46.35	-72.55	14:16:22	210	47	–	–	–	–	16:37:29	18	28	15:28:49	111	39	234	0.986	0.989		
Verdun	45.45	-73.57	14:14:26	211	49	15:26:36.1	322	15:28:26.3	259	16:36:53	16	29	15:27:33	111	40	233	1.051	1.000	0.854	01m51s

Table 2–11: Local Circumstances for North Atlantic

Location	Lat °	Long °	First Contact Time h m s	V °	Alt °	Second Contact Time h m s	V °	Third Contact Time h m s	V °	Fourth Contact Time h m s	V °	Alt °	Middle Eclipse Time h m s	V °	Alt °	Azm °	Ecl. Mag.	Ecl. Obs.	FDCL	Durat Total
Azores																				
Ponta Delgada	37.73	-25.67	19:05:26	210	12	–	–	–	–	–	–	–	20:00:16	283	2	278	0.690	0.619		
Bermuda																				
Hamilton	32.28	-64.77	15:26:18	215	52	–	–	–	–	17:37:34	333	26	16:34:27	271	39	252	0.561	0.466		
Greenland																				
Egedesminde	68.70	-52.75	16:40:06	189	22	–	–	–	–	18:19:06	75	14	17:30:14	131	18	244	0.445	0.336		
Godthab	64.18	-51.73	16:39:39	193	24	–	–	–	–	18:28:16	62	13	17:34:55	127	19	247	0.566	0.471		
Holsteinsborg	66.92	-53.67	16:39:21	191	23	–	–	–	–	18:22:32	70	14	17:31:41	130	19	244	0.489	0.384		
Iceland																				
Akureyri	65.73	-18.13	18:49:30	189	10	–	–	–	–	20:24:53	71	0	19:37:57	130	5	279	0.514	0.411		
Reykjavik	64.15	-21.85	18:49:25	190	11	–	–	–	–	20:28:31	66	1	19:39:51	128	6	276	0.562	0.466		
St. Pierre & Miquelon																				
St. Pierre	46.78	-56.18	16:36:08	205	37	–	–	–	–	18:47:04	14	16	17:43:53	288	26	252	0.976	0.978		

Table 2–12: Local Circumstances for Mexico

Location	Lat	Long	First Contact Time	V	Alt	Second Contact Time	V	Third Contact Time	V	Fourth Contact Time	V	Alt	Middle Eclipse Time	V	Alt	Azm	Ecl. Mag.	Ecl. Obs.	FDCL	Durat Total
	°	°	h m s	°	°	h m s	°	h m s	°	h m s	°	°	h m s	°	°	°				
Mexico																				
Acapulco	16.86	-99.89	10:49:46	309	61	-	-	-	-	13:29:23	338	75	12:07:40	355	78	138	0.751	0.698		
Aguascalientes	21.88	-102.30	10:54:27	291	59	-	-	-	-	13:36:45	2	72	12:13:45	346	73	147	0.915	0.906		
Campeche	19.85	-90.54	11:14:38	292	73	-	-	-	-	13:48:28	320	62	12:31:09	287	76	209	0.605	0.519		
Cancun	21.16	-86.85	12:25:47	274	75	-	-	-	-	14:55:48	318	57	13:41:01	274	72	225	0.559	0.464		
Celaya	20.53	-100.82	10:54:21	296	60	-	-	-	-	13:36:21	352	72	12:13:34	344	75	149	0.853	0.827		
Chihuahua	28.64	-106.09	10:03:04	271	54	-	-	-	-	12:41:18	32	67	11:20:30	162	66	151	0.918	0.909		
Chilpancingo	17.55	-99.50	10:51:36	306	62	-	-	-	-	13:31:34	338	74	12:09:46	350	78	143	0.757	0.706		
Chimalhuacan	19.44	-98.95	10:55:44	300	63	-	-	-	-	13:36:44	342	71	12:14:37	339	77	154	0.786	0.742		
Ciudad Acuna	29.32	-100.93	12:10:51	268	59	13:28:22.6	17	13:31:47.3	273	14:51:32	14	63	13:30:06	145	68	170	1.056	1.000	0.632	03m26s
Ciudad Apodaca	25.78	-100.19	11:05:02	279	61	-	-	-	-	13:47:21	3	66	12:24:54	328	71	166	0.953	0.953		
Ciudad Benito Ju	25.65	-100.09	11:04:56	279	61	-	-	-	-	13:47:17	2	66	12:24:49	328	71	166	0.948	0.947		
Ciudad Lopez Mat	19.56	-99.25	10:55:24	300	62	-	-	-	-	13:36:35	343	72	12:14:21	340	77	153	0.796	0.754		
Ciudad Nicolas R	19.62	-99.31	10:55:23	299	62	-	-	-	-	13:36:38	344	72	12:14:21	340	77	153	0.799	0.758		
Ciudad Obregon	27.49	-109.93	09:56:38	273	50	-	-	-	-	12:32:13	48	70	11:12:20	173	64	137	0.861	0.836		
Ciudad Victoria	23.74	-99.15	11:02:54	285	62	-	-	-	-	13:45:22	354	67	12:22:49	327	73	166	0.885	0.868		
Coacalco de Berr	19.63	-99.09	10:55:48	299	62	-	-	-	-	13:36:58	343	71	12:14:46	339	77	154	0.794	0.751		
Cuautitlan Izcal	19.65	-99.21	10:55:36	299	62	-	-	-	-	13:36:50	343	71	12:14:35	339	77	154	0.797	0.755		
Cuernavaca	18.92	-99.23	10:54:21	302	62	-	-	-	-	13:35:09	341	72	12:13:03	342	77	150	0.781	0.736		
Culiacan	24.79	-107.40	09:53:29	281	53	-	-	-	-	12:33:01	32	72	11:11:07	174	68	138	0.968	0.970		
Durango	24.02	-104.65	10:55:16	284	56	12:12:07.6	112	12:15:56.5	224	13:36:43	17	71	12:14:03	348	70	144	1.057	1.000	-0.543	03m46s
Ecatepec	19.61	-99.06	10:55:49	299	62	-	-	-	-	13:36:58	343	71	12:14:46	339	77	154	0.792	0.750		
El Salto	23.78	-105.36	10:53:52	285	55	12:10:12.6	92	12:14:35.8	250	13:35:02	20	72	12:12:25	351	70	141	1.057	1.000	-0.172	04m24s
Ensenada	31.86	-116.61	10:01:42	259	44	-	-	-	-	12:23:35	81	65	11:10:38	177	57	132	0.648	0.570		
Escuinapa de Hid	22.85	-105.77	10:51:29	288	55	12:07:59.2	118	12:11:49.2	231	13:32:39	21	73	12:09:55	354	70	137	1.057	1.000	-0.535	03m46s
General Escobedo	25.81	-100.33	11:04:53	279	60	-	-	-	-	13:47:10	4	66	12:24:43	328	71	166	0.957	0.957		
Gomez Palacio	25.56	-103.50	10:59:52	280	57	12:16:45.6	89	12:21:03.4	232	13:41:22	15	69	12:18:56	340	70	152	1.057	1.000	-0.296	04m16s
Guadalajara	20.68	-103.34	10:50:38	295	57	-	-	-	-	13:32:38	4	74	12:09:34	353	73	138	0.913	0.904		
Guadalupe	25.68	-100.23	11:04:46	279	61	-	-	-	-	13:47:06	3	66	12:24:38	328	71	166	0.952	0.951		
Hermosillo	29.10	-110.95	09:59:18	268	49	-	-	-	-	12:32:21	54	68	11:13:48	172	63	138	0.809	0.770		
Irapuato	20.67	-101.35	10:53:44	296	60	-	-	-	-	13:35:50	355	72	12:12:57	346	75	147	0.868	0.846		
Ixtapaluca	19.32	-98.88	10:55:40	301	63	-	-	-	-	13:36:34	341	71	12:14:30	339	77	154	0.782	0.737		
Juarez	31.74	-106.49	11:09:20	262	53	-	-	-	-	13:44:27	38	64	12:25:27	157	64	156	0.847	0.819		
La Paz	24.14	-110.31	09:49:00	282	50	-	-	-	-	12:26:23	48	73	11:05:16	182	65	128	0.918	0.909		
Leon	21.12	-101.68	10:54:00	294	59	-	-	-	-	13:36:13	357	72	12:13:16	346	74	147	0.885	0.868		
Los Mochis	25.79	-109.00	09:53:52	278	51	-	-	-	-	12:31:33	42	72	11:10:32	175	66	136	0.914	0.904		
Matamoros	25.88	-97.50	12:09:32	277	63	-	-	-	-	14:51:48	355	64	13:29:44	317	72	178	0.898	0.884		
Mazatlan	23.24	-106.41	09:51:28	286	54	11:07:30.5	71	11:11:46.4	279	12:32:12	25	73	11:09:39	175	69	136	1.057	1.000	0.252	04m18s
Merida	20.97	-89.62	11:18:19	285	73	-	-	-	-	13:52:18	322	60	12:35:07	284	74	214	0.612	0.527		
Mexicali	32.66	-115.47	10:04:18	258	45	-	-	-	-	12:26:57	76	65	11:13:43	174	57	135	0.655	0.579		
Mexico City	19.43	-99.13	10:55:24	300	62	-	-	-	-	13:36:28	342	72	12:14:17	340	77	153	0.790	0.747		
Monclova	26.91	-101.42	11:05:24	276	59	12:23:40.9	120	12:26:05.4	181	13:47:08	10	66	12:24:55	330	70	164	1.057	1.000	-0.855	02m20s
Monterrey	25.67	-100.31	11:04:39	279	60	-	-	-	-	13:46:58	3	66	12:24:30	328	71	166	0.953	0.953		
Morelia	19.70	-101.19	10:52:16	299	60	-	-	-	-	13:34:01	351	73	12:11:15	349	75	144	0.843	0.815		
Naucalpan	19.48	-99.24	10:55:16	300	62	-	-	-	-	13:36:25	343	72	12:14:11	340	77	153	0.794	0.751		
Nava	28.42	-100.77	11:09:18	271	59	12:26:34.3	68	12:30:56.8	224	13:50:33	11	64	12:28:47	326	69	169	1.056	1.000	-0.183	04m23s
Nezahualcoyotl	19.40	-98.99	10:55:36	300	63	-	-	-	-	13:36:36	342	71	12:14:28	339	77	154	0.786	0.742		
Nogales	31.32	-110.95	10:04:20	263	49	-	-	-	-	12:35:05	56	66	11:17:54	168	62	143	0.767	0.717		
Nueva Rosita	27.94	-101.22	11:07:43	272	59	12:24:57.4	72	12:29:18.4	224	13:49:04	12	65	12:27:09	328	69	166	1.056	1.000	-0.224	04m21s
Nuevo Laredo	27.49	-99.51	12:09:19	273	61	-	-	-	-	14:51:14	5	64	13:29:13	323	70	172	0.976	0.980		
Oaxaca	17.07	-96.72	10:56:25	309	66	-	-	-	-	13:34:03	327	71	12:13:46	334	80	159	0.681	0.611		
Ojo de Agua	19.68	-99.01	10:56:02	299	63	-	-	-	-	13:37:12	343	71	12:15:00	338	77	155	0.793	0.750		
Pachuca	20.12	-98.74	10:57:17	298	63	-	-	-	-	13:38:35	343	70	12:16:23	335	77	158	0.796	0.755		
Piedras Negras	28.70	-100.52	12:10:11	270	59	13:27:28.0	65	13:31:51.3	225	14:51:21	11	64	13:29:41	325	69	170	1.056	1.000	-0.151	04m24s
Playa del Carmen	20.63	-87.08	12:24:36	277	76	-	-	-	-	14:54:12	317	57	13:39:33	274	72	224	0.550	0.454		
Puebla	19.05	-98.20	10:56:30	302	64	-	-	-	-	13:36:54	338	71	12:15:10	336	78	157	0.760	0.709		
Queretaro	20.59	-100.39	10:55:10	296	61	-	-	-	-	13:37:08	350	72	12:14:26	342	75	151	0.844	0.816		
Reynosa	26.09	-98.28	12:08:38	277	62	-	-	-	-	14:50:57	358	64	13:28:46	320	71	175	0.919	0.911		
Sabinas	27.92	-101.12	11:07:49	272	59	12:25:07.4	77	12:29:23.3	218	13:49:12	11	65	12:27:17	328	69	167	1.056	1.000	-0.316	04m14s
Saltillo	25.43	-101.00	11:03:09	280	60	-	-	-	-	13:45:25	5	67	12:22:52	332	71	162	0.963	0.965		
San Luis Potosi	22.15	-100.97	10:57:01	291	60	-	-	-	-	13:39:25	357	71	12:16:32	340	74	153	0.891	0.876		
San Nicolas de l	25.74	-100.30	11:04:47	279	60	-	-	-	-	13:47:06	3	66	12:24:38	328	71	166	0.955	0.955		
San Pedro (Colon	25.76	-102.98	11:00:58	279	58	12:18:14.8	102	12:22:03.7	214	13:42:36	13	68	12:20:10	338	70	155	1.057	1.000	-0.543	03m46s
Santa Catarina	25.68	-100.46	11:04:25	279	60	-	-	-	-	13:46:43	4	66	12:24:15	329	71	165	0.957	0.957		
Santa Rosa de Mu	27.87	-101.50	11:07:11	273	59	12:24:19.1	64	12:28:45.8	234	13:48:28	13	65	12:26:33	329	69	165	1.056	1.000	-0.069	04m27s
Soledad de Graci	22.18	-100.94	10:57:08	291	60	-	-	-	-	13:39:32	357	70	12:16:40	339	74	154	0.891	0.876		
Tampico	22.26	-97.87	11:02:30	290	64	-	-	-	-	13:44:23	346	67	12:22:11	325	75	169	0.824	0.790		
Tehuacan	18.46	-97.39	10:57:09	304	65	-	-	-	-	13:36:38	333	71	12:15:25	333	78	160	0.728	0.669		
Tepic	21.52	-104.89	09:50:00	292	55	-	-	-	-	12:31:41	14	74	11:08:41	356	71	136	0.966	0.968		
Tijuana	32.53	-117.04	[illegible]	257	44	-	-	-	-	12:23:20	83	64	11:11:15	177	56	132	0.628	0.546		
Tlalnepantla	19.54	-99.19	[illegible]	300	62	-	-	-	-	13:36:37	343	72	12:14:23	340	77	153	0.794	0.752		
Tlaquepaque	20.64	-103.31	[illegible]	295	57	-	-	-	-	13:32:37	4	74	12:09:33	353	73	138	0.912	0.902		
Tonala	20.62	-103.25	[illegible]	295	57	-	-	-	-	13:32:41	3	74	12:09:37	353	73	139	0.910	0.899		
Torreon	25.54	-103.44	10:59:55	280	57	12:16:51.4	92	12:21:04.8	228	13:41:26	15	69	12:18:59	340	70	153	1.057	1.000	-0.352	04m11
Tuxtla Gutierrez	16.75	-93.12	11:04:17	309	71	-	-	-	-	13:37:26	316	68	12:19:53	305	81	189	0.590	0.501		
Uruapan	19.42	-102.06	10:50:20	299	59	-	-	-	-	13:32:03	355	74	12:09:11	353	75	139	0.857	0.832		
Veracruz	19.19	-96.15	11:00:49	301	66	-	-	-	-	13:40:01	332	69	12:19:10	323	78	171	0.716	0.654		
Villahermosa	17.99	-92.93	11:06:21	304	71	-	-	-	-	13:40:58	320	66	12:22:47	302	79	193	0.614	0.530		
Xalapa	19.54	-96.91	10:59:50	300	65	-	-	-	-	13:39:49	335	69	12:18:29	326	78	167	0.741	0.686		
Xico	19.29	-98.94	10:55:31	301	63	-	-	-	-	13:36:26	341	72	12:14:20	339	77	154	0.783	0.737		
Zapopan	20.72	-103.39	10:50:38	295	57	-	-	-	-	13:32:39	4	74	12:09:35	354	73	138	0.915	0.906		

Table 2–13: Local Circumstances for Central & South America

Location	Lat °	Long °	First Contact Time h m s	V °	Alt °	Second Contact Time h m s	V °	Third Contact Time h m s	V °	Fourth Contact Time h m s	V °	Alt °	Middle Eclipse Time h m s	V °	Alt °	Azm °	Ecl. Mag.	Ecl. Obs.	FDCL	Durat Total
Colombia																				
Barranquilla	10.98	-74.80	13:20:31	219	70	–	–	–	–	14:16:54	256	56	13:48:49	237	63	265	0.054	0.015		
Cartagena	10.42	-75.53	13:17:53	218	71	–	–	–	–	14:13:44	254	58	13:45:53	236	65	266	0.053	0.015		
Belize																				
Belize City	17.50	-88.20	11:18:23	296	77	–	–	–	–	13:44:29	308	61	12:31:12	273	77	223	0.496	0.393		
Costa Rica																				
Alajuela	10.02	-84.22	11:29:40	318	87	–	–	–	–	13:19:10	272	65	12:24:15	237	78	259	0.224	0.125		
Limon	10.00	-83.03	11:35:08	270	88	–	–	–	–	13:18:50	269	64	12:26:55	236	77	261	0.197	0.103		
San Jose	9.93	-84.08	11:30:18	315	87	–	–	–	–	13:18:46	271	65	12:24:23	236	78	259	0.219	0.121		
El Salvador																				
San Miguel	13.48	-88.18	11:15:11	319	79	–	–	–	–	13:31:42	294	65	12:22:59	264	81	231	0.399	0.288		
San Salvador	13.70	-89.20	11:12:04	320	77	–	–	–	–	13:31:45	296	66	12:21:19	271	82	223	0.427	0.318		
Santa Ana	13.98	-89.57	11:11:09	319	76	–	–	–	–	13:32:25	298	66	12:21:10	275	82	220	0.442	0.334		
Guatemala																				
Escuintla	14.30	-90.78	11:07:48	319	74	–	–	–	–	13:32:29	302	67	12:19:21	286	82	208	0.478	0.373		
Guatemala	14.63	-90.52	11:08:53	317	75	–	–	–	–	13:33:45	302	67	12:20:36	283	82	211	0.480	0.375		
Honduras																				
San Pedro Sula	15.45	-88.03	11:17:06	307	78	–	–	–	–	13:38:21	301	63	12:27:23	269	79	227	0.443	0.334		
Tegucigalpa	14.10	-87.22	11:18:48	312	80	–	–	–	–	13:34:26	294	64	12:26:18	261	79	234	0.391	0.280		
Nicaragua																				
Leon	12.43	-86.88	11:19:07	322	81	–	–	–	–	13:28:38	287	65	12:23:31	254	80	241	0.343	0.232		
Managua	12.15	-86.28	11:21:13	321	82	–	–	–	–	13:27:48	285	65	12:24:13	251	80	245	0.323	0.212		
Masaya	11.97	-86.10	11:21:51	321	83	–	–	–	–	13:27:10	284	65	12:24:13	250	80	246	0.314	0.204		
Panama																				
Colon	9.37	-79.90	12:52:30	211	82	–	–	–	–	14:13:22	260	62	13:32:59	232	72	266	0.113	0.046		
David	8.43	-82.43	12:39:40	214	88	–	–	–	–	14:10:26	260	65	13:24:58	229	77	267	0.145	0.066		
Panama City	8.97	-79.53	12:55:38	209	81	–	–	–	–	14:10:21	256	63	13:33:02	231	72	267	0.095	0.035		

Table 2–14: Local Circumstances for the Caribbean

Location	Lat °	Long °	First Contact Time h m s	V °	Alt °	Second Contact Time h m s	V °	Third Contact Time h m s	V °	Fourth Contact Time h m s	V °	Alt °	Middle Eclipse Time h m s	V °	Alt °	Azm °	Ecl. Mag.	Ecl. Obs.	FDCL	Durat Total
Antigua & Barbuda																				
St. Johns	17.12	-61.85	15:01:51	232	47	–	–	–	–	15:52:42	270	35	15:27:36	251	41	265	0.055	0.016		
Bahamas																				
Freeport	26.50	-78.75	13:52:00	232	69	–	–	–	–	16:16:16	324	43	15:05:41	269	58	239	0.554	0.458		
Nassau	25.08	-77.35	13:55:16	229	70	–	–	–	–	16:14:33	318	43	15:06:29	265	57	243	0.491	0.387		
Cayman Islands																				
Georgetown	19.30	-81.38	12:40:57	248	78	–	–	–	–	14:55:38	303	52	13:49:02	259	67	242	0.401	0.290		
Cuba																				
Camaguey	21.38	-77.92	13:52:50	231	73	–	–	–	–	16:04:34	306	47	14:59:55	260	61	246	0.395	0.284		
Guantanamo	20.13	-75.20	14:02:20	224	71	–	–	–	–	16:02:41	299	45	15:03:46	256	58	251	0.315	0.205		
Holguin	20.88	-76.25	13:58:26	226	72	–	–	–	–	16:04:20	302	45	15:02:40	258	59	249	0.353	0.242		
Havana	23.13	-82.37	13:39:58	248	74	–	–	–	–	16:05:14	317	50	14:53:32	268	65	235	0.522	0.422		
Santa Clara	22.40	-79.97	13:46:36	239	74	–	–	–	–	16:05:38	312	48	14:57:15	263	63	241	0.459	0.352		
Santiago de Cuba	20.02	-75.82	14:00:12	225	72	–	–	–	–	16:01:53	299	45	15:02:16	256	59	251	0.321	0.211		
Dominican Republic																				
Santiago	19.45	-70.70	14:19:29	220	64	–	–	–	–	16:02:50	291	41	15:12:24	253	52	257	0.228	0.128		
Santo Domingo	18.47	-69.90	14:24:10	221	63	–	–	–	–	15:59:12	286	41	15:12:45	252	52	259	0.188	0.096		
Haiti																				
Cap-Haïtien	19.75	-72.20	15:13:31	220	66	–	–	–	–	17:03:10	294	42	16:09:37	254	54	255	0.258	0.153		
Gonaïves	19.45	-72.68	15:12:02	221	67	–	–	–	–	17:01:49	293	43	16:08:09	254	55	255	0.256	0.152		
Port-au-Prince	18.53	-72.33	15:14:26	220	67	–	–	–	–	16:58:29	289	43	16:07:34	252	55	256	0.224	0.125		
Jamaica																				
Kingston	18.00	-76.80	12:57:28	226	74	–	–	–	–	14:54:17	292	48	13:56:49	253	62	252	0.282	0.174		
Spanish Town	17.98	-76.95	12:56:54	226	74	–	–	–	–	14:54:09	293	49	13:56:28	253	62	252	0.284	0.176		
Montserrat																				
Plymouth	16.70	-62.22	15:02:51	233	47	–	–	–	–	15:49:31	268	36	15:26:26	250	41	265	0.046	0.012		
Puerto Rico																				
Bayamon	18.40	-66.15	14:39:09	223	56	–	–	–	–	16:00:06	282	37	15:20:31	252	46	262	0.139	0.062		
Carolina	18.38	-65.95	14:39:59	223	56	–	–	–	–	16:00:04	282	37	15:20:55	252	46	262	0.136	0.060		
Ponce	18.02	-66.62	14:38:25	223	57	–	–	–	–	15:58:05	281	38	15:19:05	251	47	262	0.133	0.058		
San Juan	18.47	-66.12	14:39:06	223	56	–	–	–	–	16:00:26	282	37	15:20:40	252	46	262	0.140	0.063		
St. Kitts & Nevis																				
Basseterre	17.30	-62.72	14:57:11	230	49	–	–	–	–	15:54:11	273	35	15:26:07	251	42	265	0.069	0.022		
Turks & Caicos Is.																				
Grand Turk	21.47	-71.13	13:15:38	220	64	–	–	–	–	15:09:40	299	39	14:14:10	257	52	254	0.294	0.185		
Virgin Is. (UK)																				
Road Town, Torto	18.43	-64.62	14:45:00	225	53	–	–	–	–	16:00:39	281	35	15:23:39	252	44	263	0.123	0.052		
Virgin Is. (US)																				
Charlotte Am., S	18.35	-64.93	14:44:03	225	54	–	–	–	–	16:00:09	281	36	15:22:55	252	45	262	0.124	0.052		

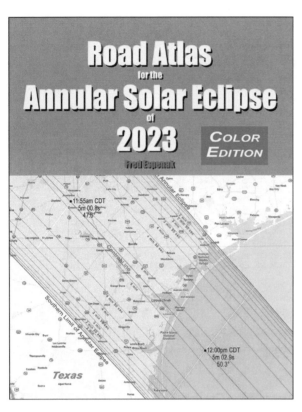

The **Road Atlas for the Annular Solar Eclipse of 2023** contains 29 maps of the **2023 Oct 14** path of annularity across the USA, Mexico, Central and South America. The large scale (1 inch ≈ 28 miles) shows both major and minor roads, towns and cities, rivers, lakes, parks, national forests, wilderness areas and mountain ranges.

Although a partial eclipse will be seen from most of North and South America, the annular phase in which the Moon is completely silhouetted in front of the Sun (known as annularity) will only be seen from within the 115 to 137 mile wide path of the Moon's antumbral shadow as it sweeps across the United States (Oregon, California, Idaho, Nevada, Utah, Colorado, Arizona, New Mexico, and Texas), Mexico, Central and South America.

Armed with this atlas and the latest weather forecasts, the road warrior is ready to chase annularity no matter where it takes you along the entire path. This mobile strategy offers the highest probability of witnessing the fascinating 2023 annular eclipse in clear skies.

For more information visit
http://astropixels.com/pubs/index.html

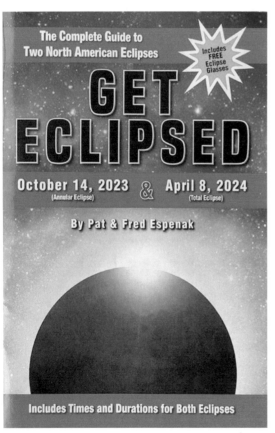

On October 14, 2023, an annular eclipse of the Sun occurs in western USA and Mexico. Six months later, an incomparable total eclipse of the Sun occurs on April 8, 2024. Its 125-mile wide path crosses Mexico, the USA from Texas to Maine, and eastern Canada.

During each event, a partial eclipse of the Sun will be visible from most of North America. The last annular eclipse visible from the USA was in 2012, while the last total eclipse was in 2017. The next total eclipse to cross the USA won't be until 2045. Don't miss the incredible experience of seeing these celestial wonders!

American Paper Optics teams up with eclipse expert, Fred Espenak and his eclipse chasing wife Pat Espenak, to bring you *Get Eclipsed*. This convenient 50-page guide to the 2023 and 2024 solar eclipses provides an in-depth look at both of these amazing events.

Get Eclipsed is an easy to read, family friendly, inexpensive eclipse guide for the entire family. It tells you everything you need to know about the upcoming annular and total eclipses of the Sun in 2023 and 2024. And it even comes with **two pairs of eclipse glasses** for safely watching the partial eclipse and annularity.

If you've never seen either an annular or a total eclipse of the Sun, this 50-page pocket guide is for you!

For more information visit
http://astropixels.com/pubs/index.html

Section 3: Detailed Maps of the Umbral Path

3.1 Introduction

The path of totality is plotted on a series of detailed maps appearing in Maps 1 to 11. The maps have a fixed scale with a small overlap, and cover the entire umbral path across Mexico, the USA, and Canada.

The map scale is ~1:3,379,000, which corresponds to 1 cm ≈ 33.8 km (1 inch ≈ 53.3 miles). This is a large enough to show major roads and highways, towns and cities, rivers, lakes, parks, national forests, wilderness areas and mountain ranges. A map reference scale (miles and kilometers) appears at the bottom of each map.

The umbral path across North America ranges in width from 199 km (123.7 mi) along Mexico's Pacific coast to a 162 km (100.6 mi) in Newfoundland. It is depicted on each map as a lightly shaded region with the northern and southern path limits clearly labeled. The total eclipse can be seen only inside this path (a partial eclipse is visible outside the path). The closer one gets to the central line, the longer the total eclipse lasts. Curves of constant total eclipse duration are marked and labeled in 30 second intervals. This makes it easy to quickly estimate the duration from any location inside the umbral path.

The local time of mid-eclipse is marked by a series of white lines crossing the umbral eclipse path at 5 minute intervals. The eclipse circumstances on the central line are labeled with the local time of mid-eclipse, the duration of totality (minutes and seconds) and the altitude of the Sun. Addition information and local circumstances at each point can be found in Tables 1–1 through 1–6.

The northern or southern limits of the path of totality cross through a number of cities and large metropolitan areas. In such cases, the duration of totality is strongly dependent on the exact location in the city. Some locations in a given city may actually lie outside the path and experience only a partial eclipse. Maps 12 to 27 show closeups of sixteen of these cities.

There are seven cities located on or just inside the northern limit of the path of totality: Dallas, TX, Fort Worth, TX, Fort Smith, AR, Fort Wayne, IN, Toledo, OH, Hamilton, ON, and Montreal, QB. Unfortunately, downtown Toronto, ON, narrowly misses totality; it is located 10 kilometers (6 miles) north of the northern eclipse path limit.

There are nine cities on or just inside the southern limit including Austin, TX, San Antonio, TX, Texarkana, TX, Little Rock, AR, Canton, OH, Columbus, OH, Youngstown, OH, Syracuse, NY, and Moncton, NB.

Maps 12 through 27 show each of these cities and includes a series of lines of constant duration of totality at 30 second intervals. This makes it possible to easily determine whether a location is in the path of totality and how long the total eclipse will last.

All the maps in Section 3 were produced using Google Maps as the underlying map with overlying eclipse graphics generated using Javascript code. A web page is available to the user for examining any part of the 2024 eclipse path at a range of zoom magnifications. An added benefit of the web page is that it automatically calculates the local circumstances for any point the user chooses, with just the click of a mouse. For more information and to access the interactive 2024 eclipse path plotted on Google Maps, visit:

www.eclipsewise.com/news/2024/.html

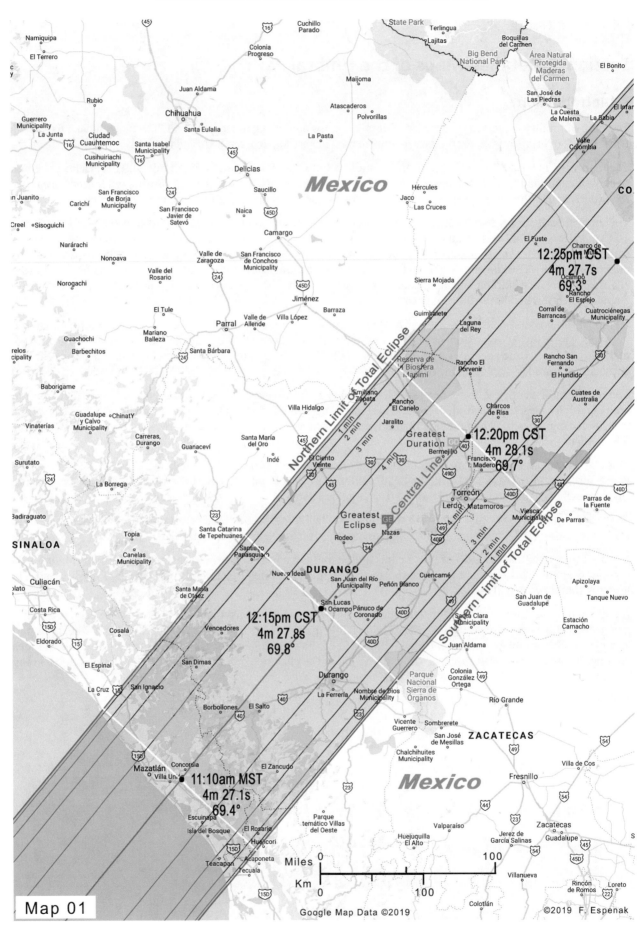

Map 01

Google Map Data ©2019

©2019 F. Espenak

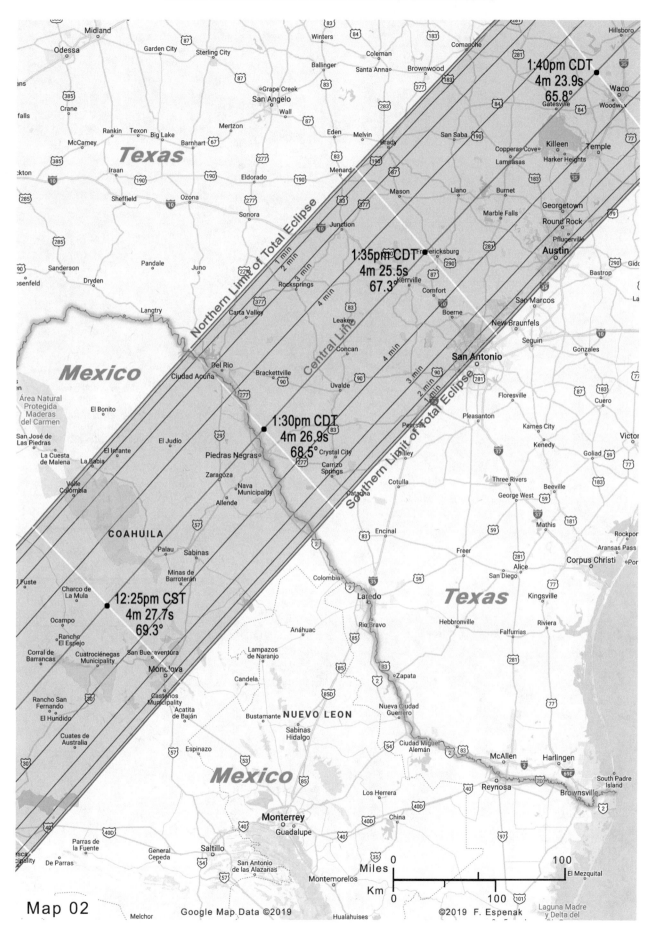

1:40pm CDT
4m 23.9s
65.8°

1:35pm CDT
4m 25.5s
67.3°

1:30pm CDT
4m 26.9s
68.5°

12:25pm CST
4m 27.7s
69.3°

Northern Limit of Total Eclipse

Central Line

Southern Limit of Total Eclipse

Texas

Mexico

Área Natural
Protegida
Maderas
del Carmen

COAHUILA

NUEVO LEON

Mexico

Map 02

Google Map Data ©2019

©2019 F. Espenak

Miles

Km

0

0

100

100

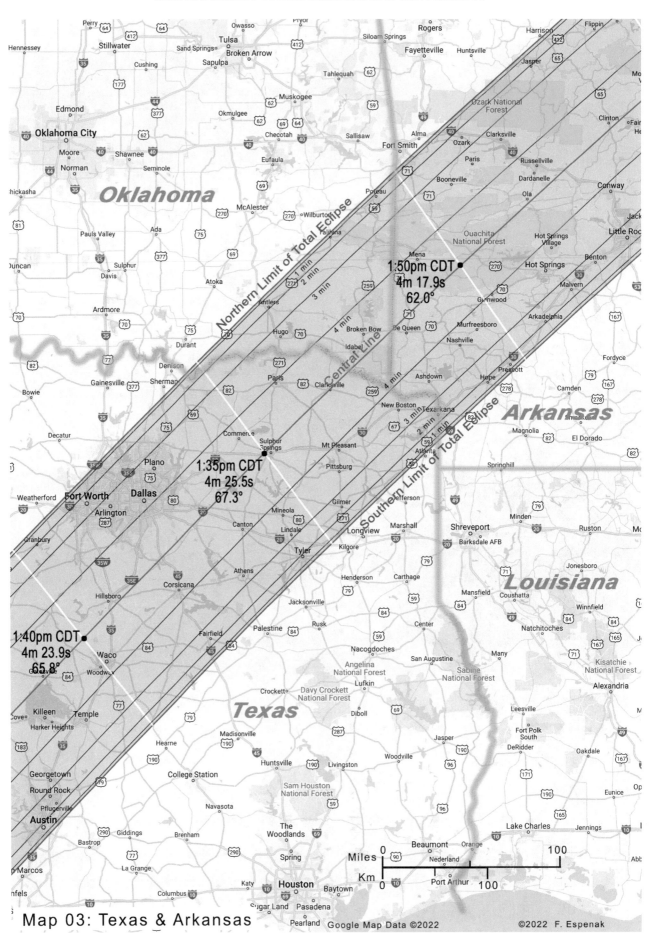

Map 03: Texas & Arkansas

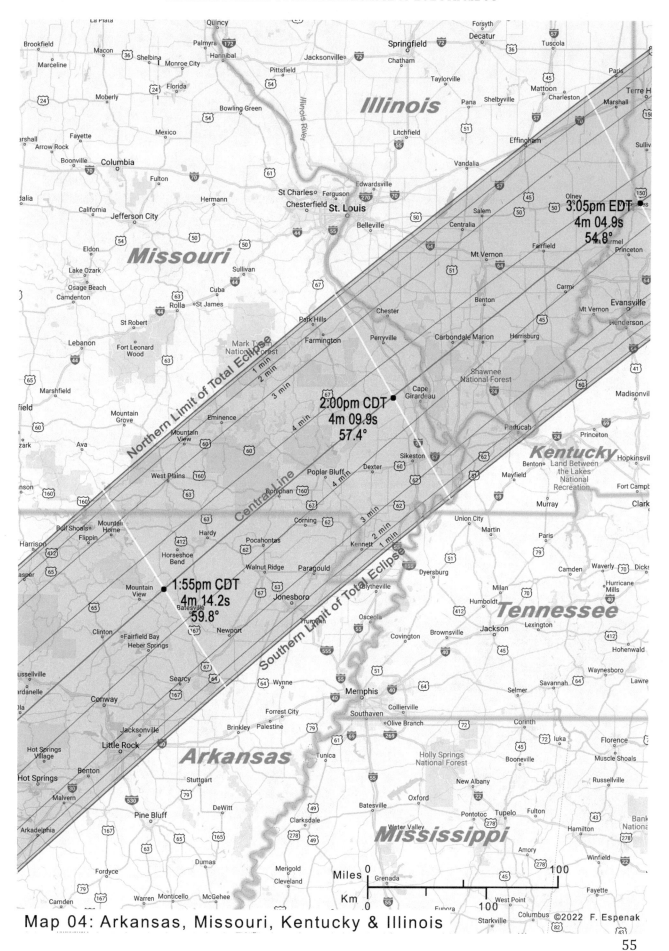

Map 04: Arkansas, Missouri, Kentucky & Illinois

©2022 F. Espenak

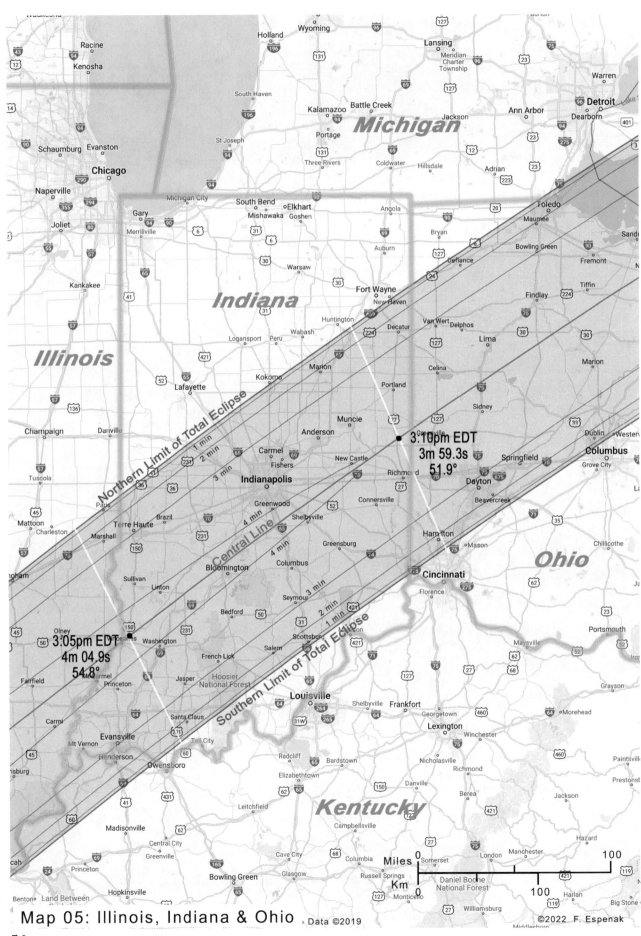

Map 05: Illinois, Indiana & Ohio

Data ©2019

©2022 F. Espenak

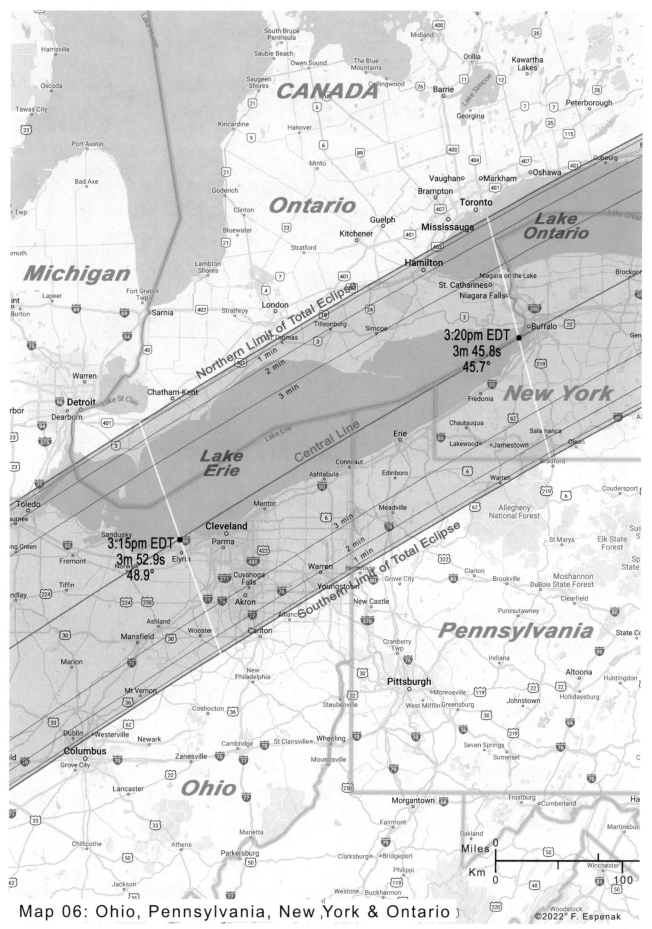

3:20pm EDT
3m 45.8s
45.7°

3:15pm EDT
3m 52.9s
48.9°

Map 06: Ohio, Pennsylvania, New York & Ontario

©2022 F. Espenak

57

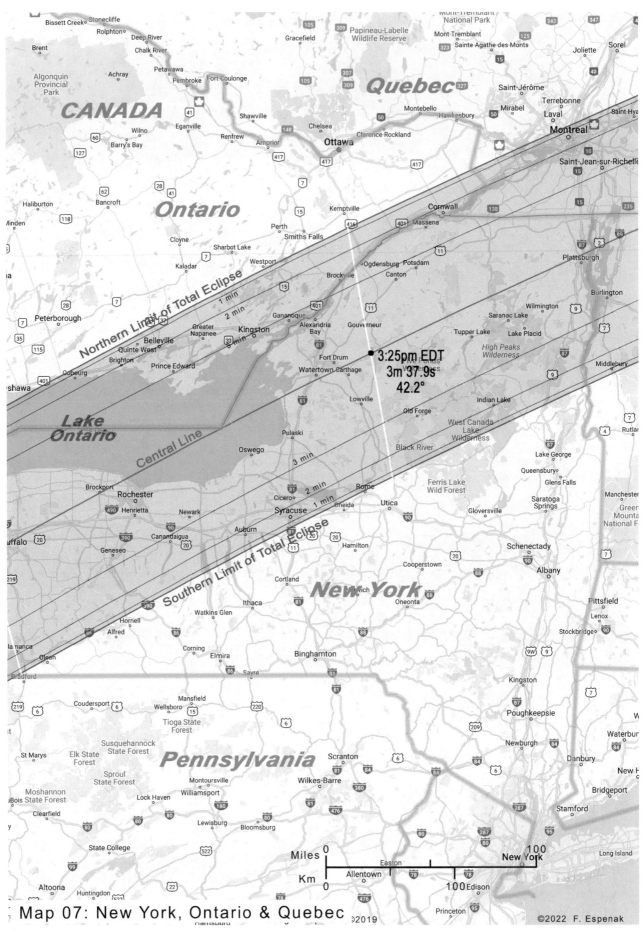

Map 07: New York, Ontario & Quebec

©2022 F. Espenak

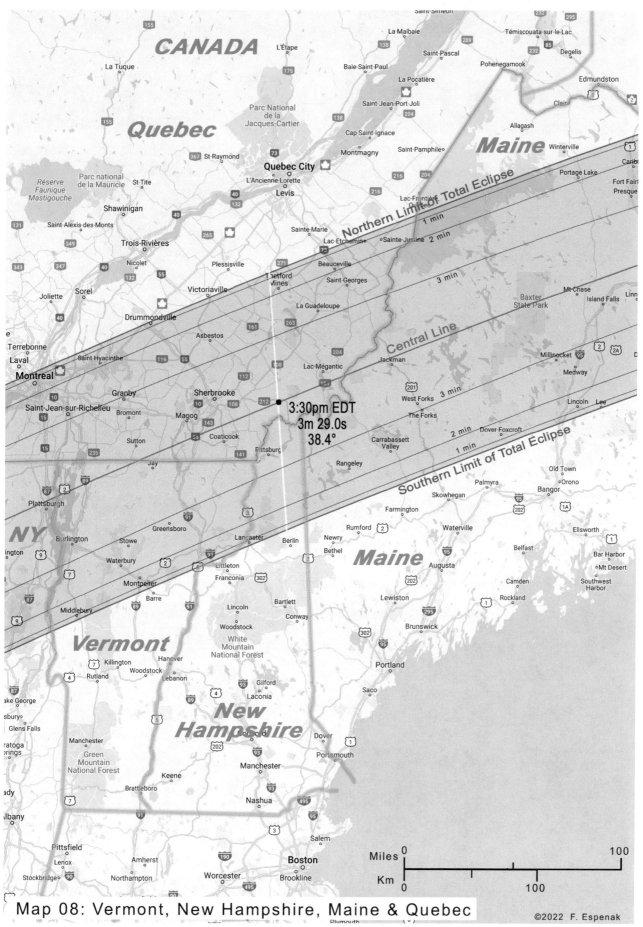

Map 08: Vermont, New Hampshire, Maine & Quebec

©2022 F. Espenak

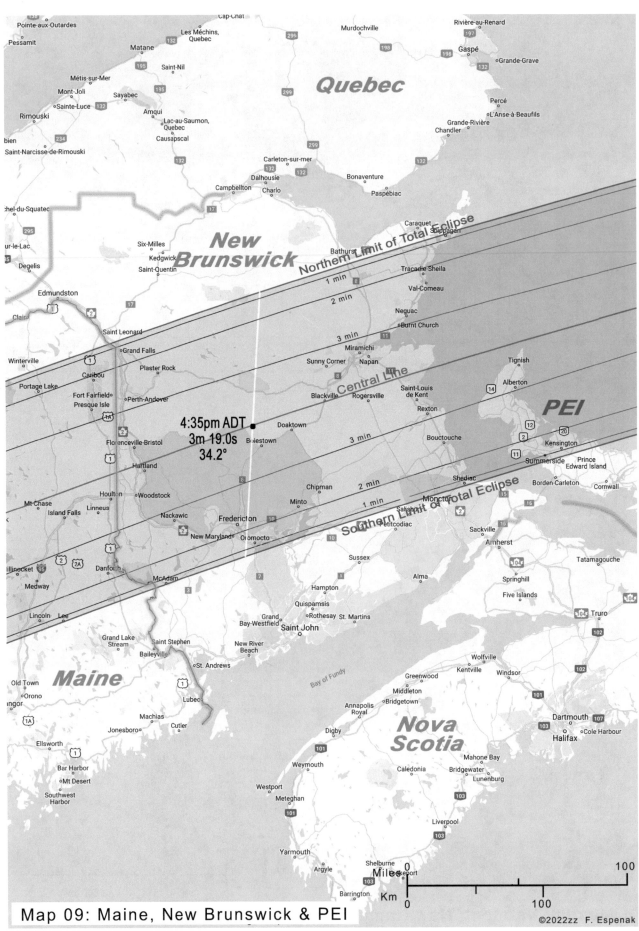

Map 09: Maine, New Brunswick & PEI

©2022zz F. Espenak

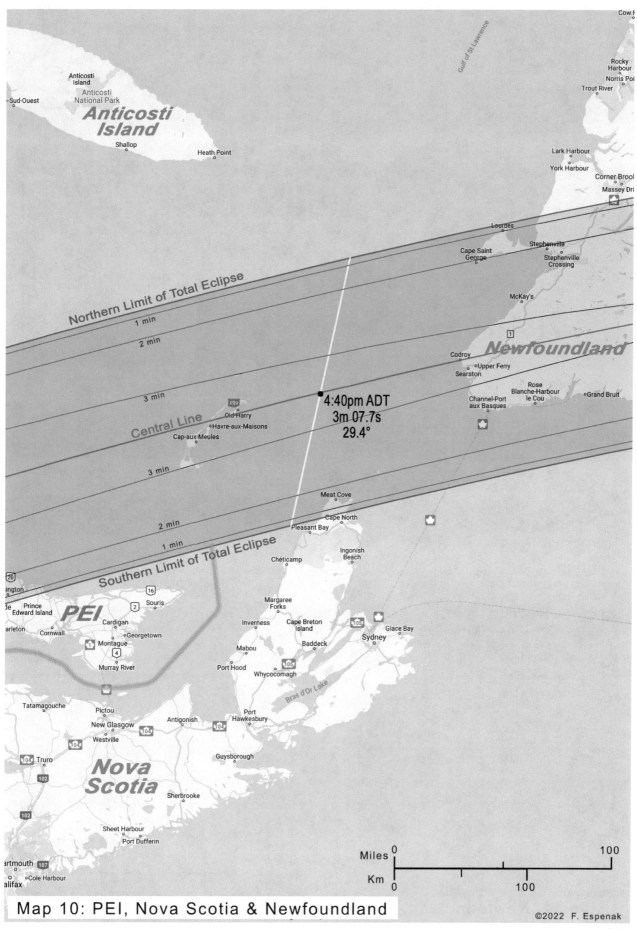

Map 10: PEI, Nova Scotia & Newfoundland

©2022 F. Espenak

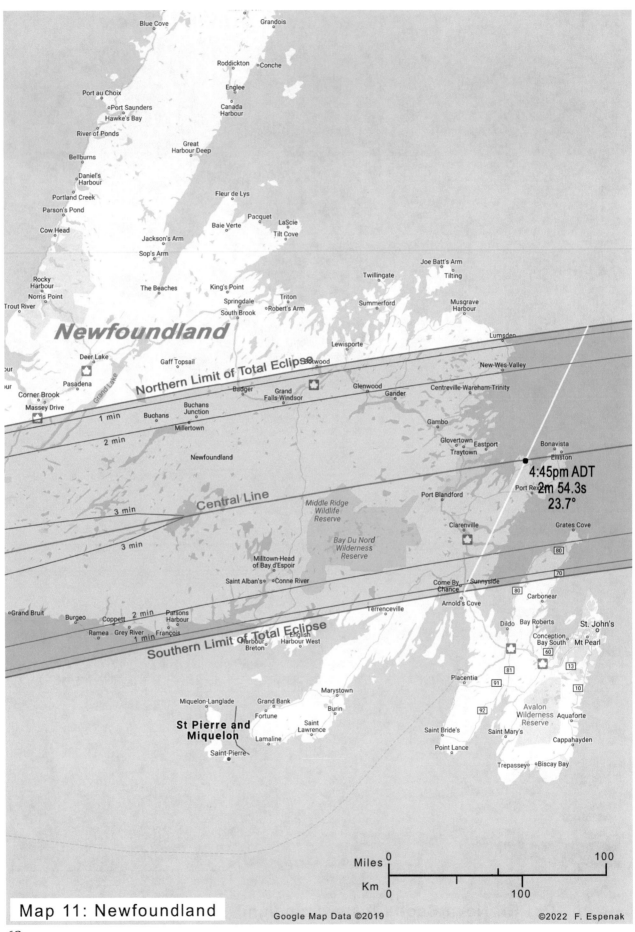

Map 11: Newfoundland

Google Map Data ©2019

©2022 F. Espenak

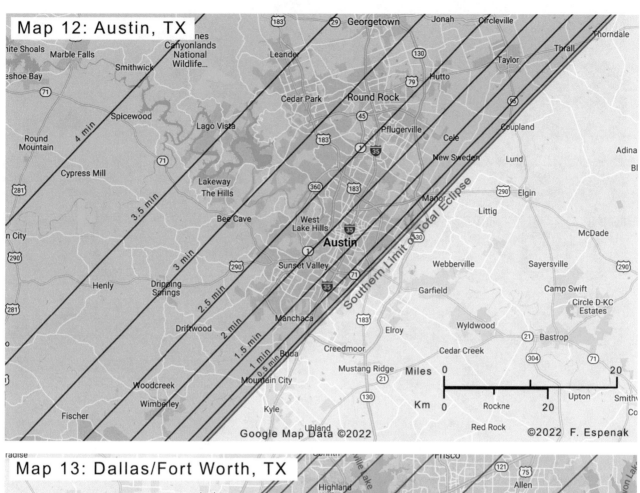

Map 12: Austin, TX

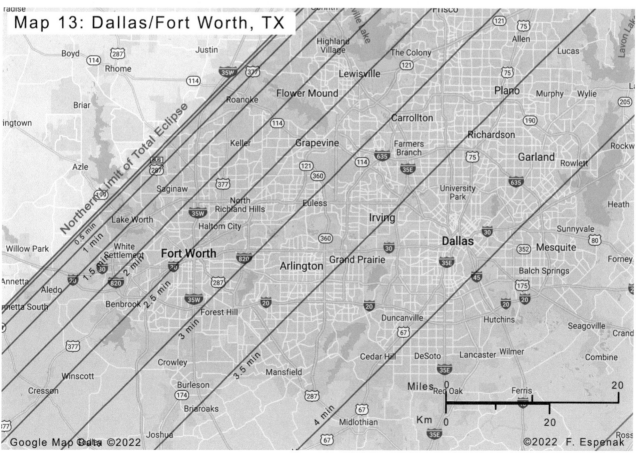

Map 13: Dallas/Fort Worth, TX

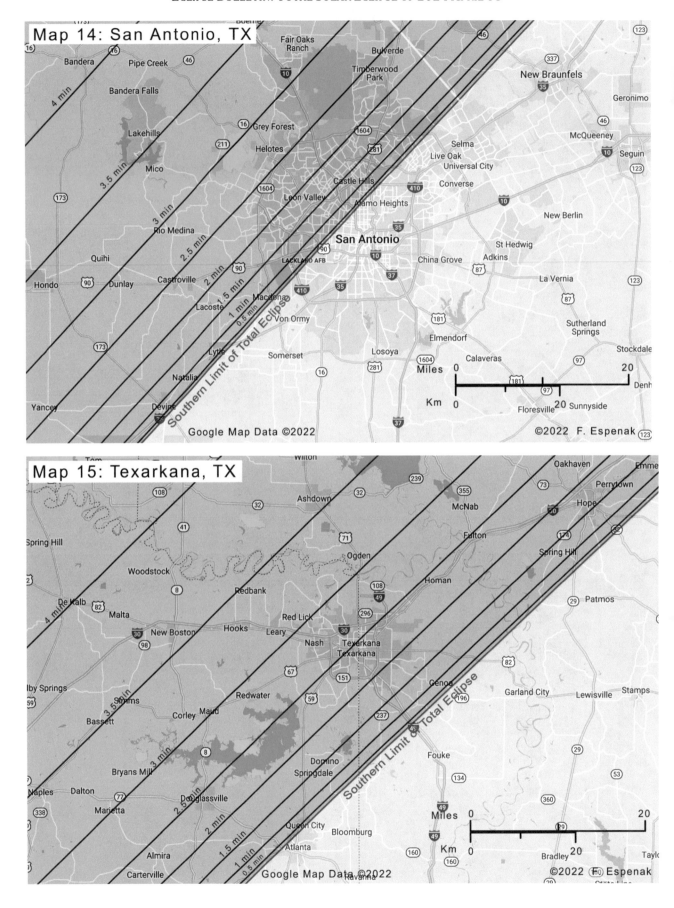

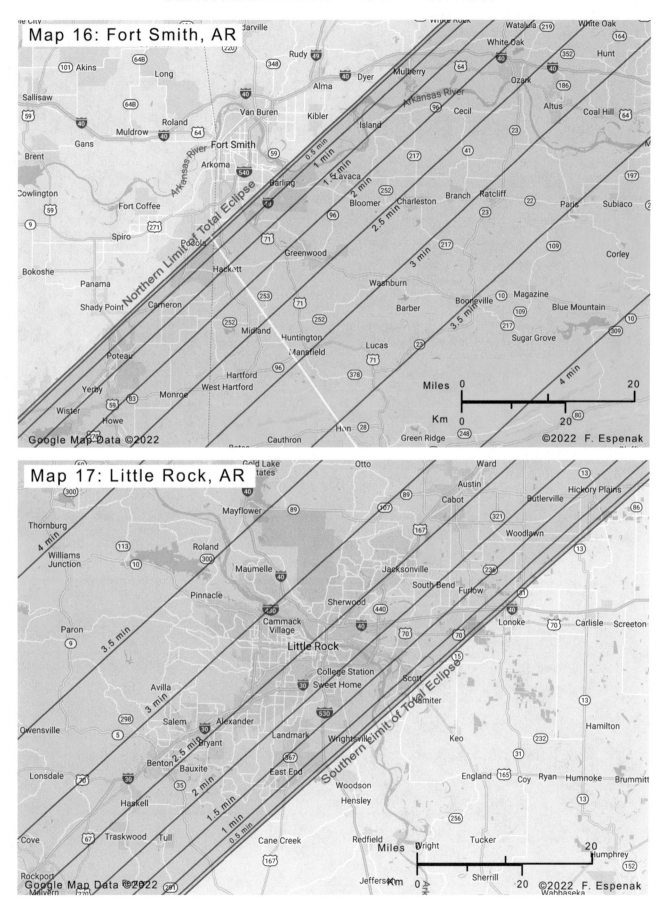

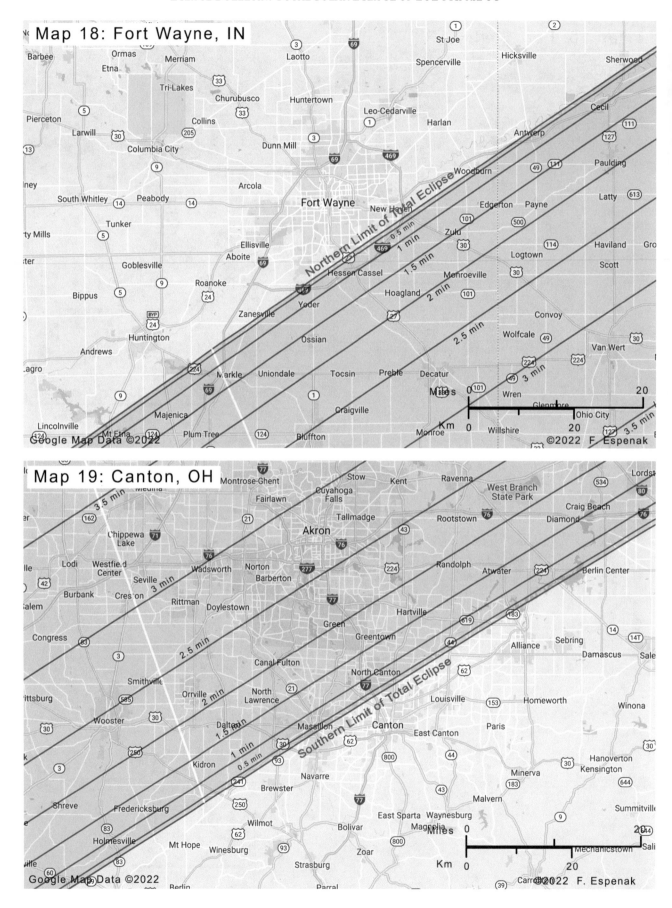

Map 18: Fort Wayne, IN

Map 19: Canton, OH

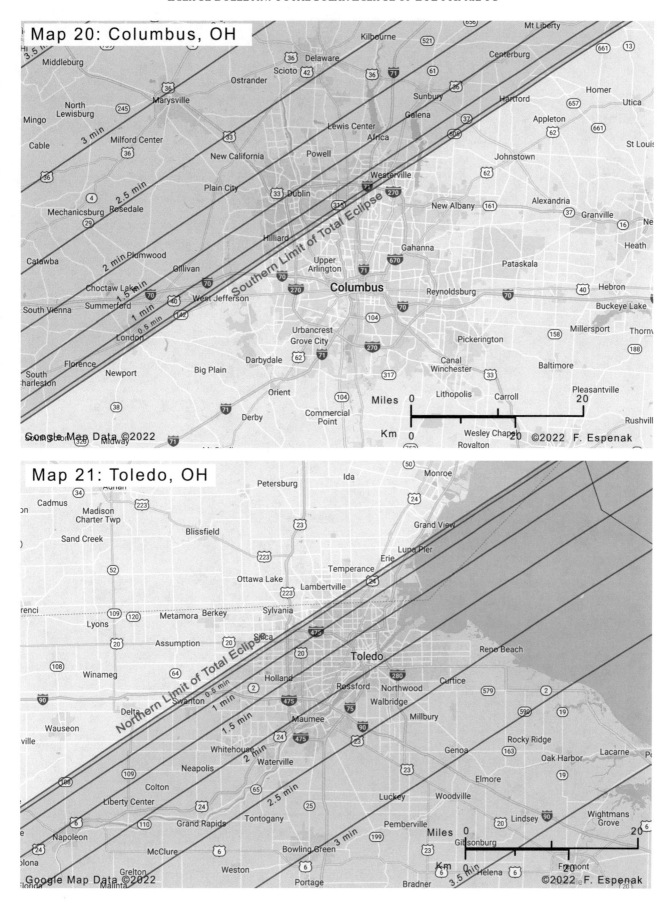

Map 20: Columbus, OH

Map 21: Toledo, OH

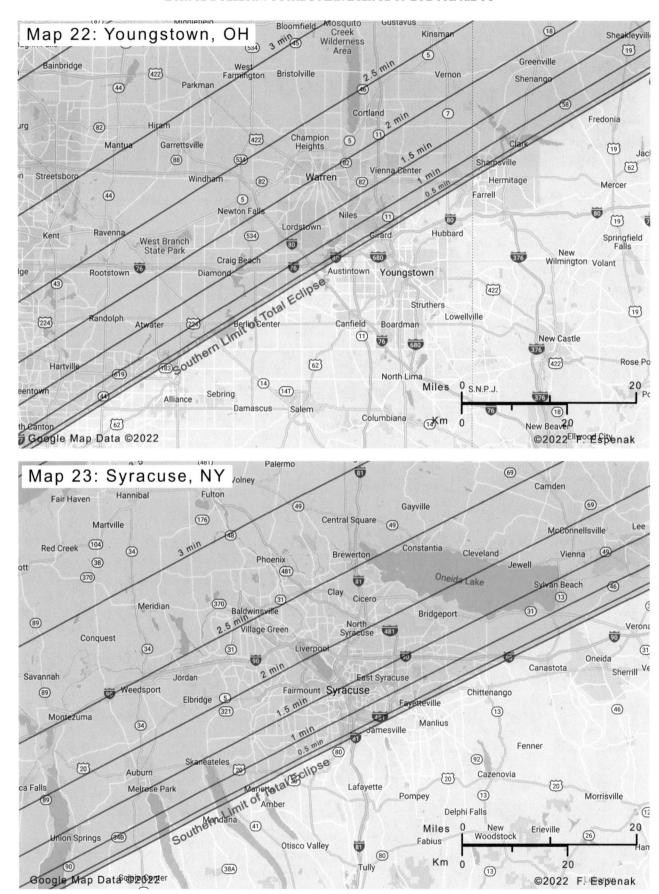

Map 22: Youngstown, OH

Map 23: Syracuse, NY

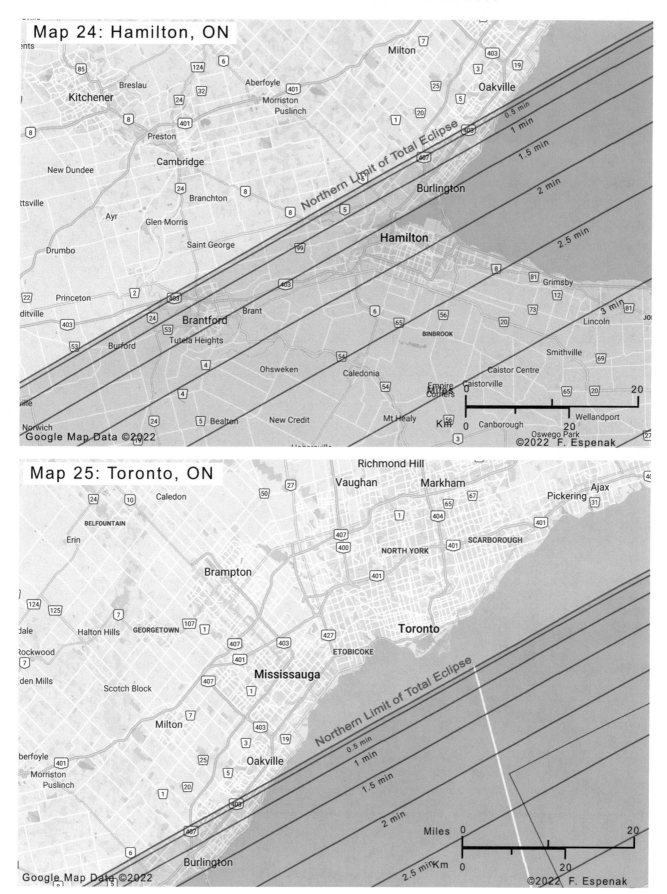

Map 24: Hamilton, ON

Map 25: Toronto, ON

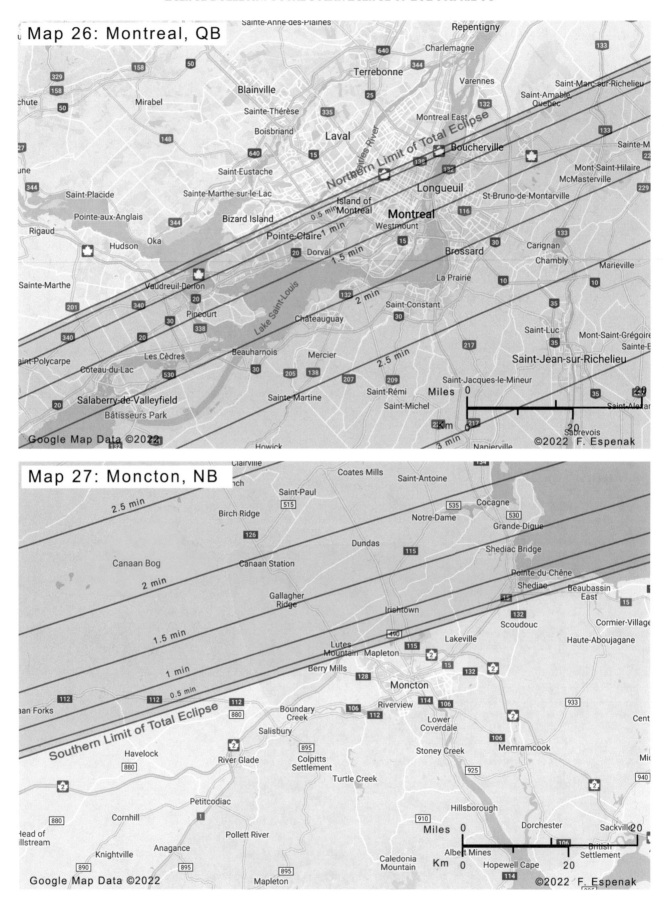

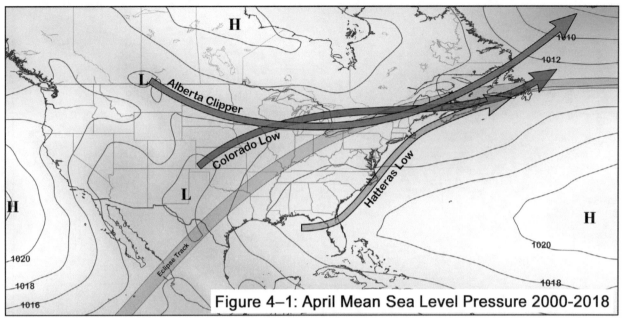

Figure 4-1: April Mean Sea Level Pressure 2000-2018

Figure 4-1: 20-year average of sea level pressure and the location of major storm tracks in April.

Section 4: Weather Prospects for the Eclipse

4.1 An Overview of April's Climate

North America's second total eclipse of the past seven years comes at a very different season than 2017. April is a month of transition across the continent, with winter storms gradually giving way to the convective buildups of spring and summer. In Mexico, the winter dry season is in its last month before the summer rains begin. Over the United States, southern parts of the track are already well into the thunderstorm season, while to the north, spring storms and occasional light snow still hint of the departing winter. In Maritime Canada, the last of the winter snow has yet to melt and fresh snowfalls are a threat with every weather system.

In April, two high-pressure systems straddle the North American continent, one northeast of Hawaii in the Pacific, the other between Bermuda and the Azores in the Atlantic. These anticyclones are just beginning to strengthen from their winter minimums, giving Mexico a last dry and sunny month before the summer rainy season begins. To the north, a poorly organized surface low lies along the eastern foothills of the Rocky Mountains with a low-pressure trough extending across the Great Lakes and Newfoundland to join up with a deep low near Iceland.

The low-pressure centers and their extended troughs roughly mark April's major storm tracks across North America (Figure 4-1). Three of the most important tracks—the Alberta Clipper, the Colorado Low, and the Hatteras Low (which is called a Nor'easter in New England)—converge on the eclipse track where it passes Newfoundland. These storms are large systems with extensive cloud shields and while not too likely on eclipse day, can bring grief across most of the shadow track if they do happen along. The tracks shown in Figure 4-1 are schematic, as the actual paths can be highly variable. The storms that cruise these tracks eventually end up in the semi-permanent Iceland Low, off the northeast corner of Figure 4-1.

Given the season and the scenario above, it is no surprise that cloudiness increases gradually from south to north along the track. Figure 4-2 shows the average April cloudiness along the central line across North America. Average cloud amounts range from under 40% in Mexico to over 80% in Newfoundland, but along the way there are regional pockets of lower cloudiness that offer refuge for eclipse day.

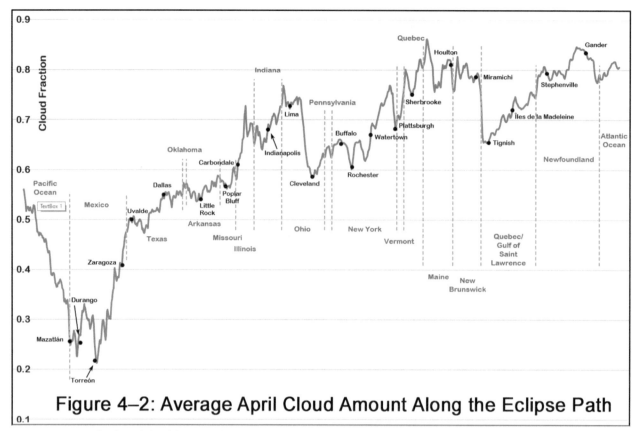

Figure 4–2: Average April Cloud Amount Along the Eclipse Path

Figure 4-2: A graph of April cloud fraction along the eclipse path across North America. These data are taken from 18 years of observations by the Aqua satellite during its 1:30 pm passage. Cloud fraction may be treated as percent cloudiness. Data: NASA.

4.2 Mexico

In the first 6600 km of its path the umbra crosses a relatively cloudy Pacific Ocean. But as the eclipse track approaches the mainland near Mazatlán, the sky gives way to the sunshine of Mexico's dry-season weather.

The Mexican coast presents an abrupt mountain barrier to the sea and so the eclipse path has only a narrow 25 km coastal plain to cross before rising over the Sierra Madre Occidental; within 100 km of the coast, the terrain has climbed to over 2600 m. The Occidentals are a rugged range with 500-m deep valley basins cutting into the mountain topography. Once across the Sierra, near Durango, the Moon's shadow enters onto the Mexican Plateau, a rough inland mesa consisting of desert plains interspersed with low mountain ridges. After a short passage, the shadow path climbs over the Sierra Madre Oriental and descends into the lowlands of the Gulf Coastal Plains and the valley of the Rio Grande.

The dry-season climatology of Northern Mexico in April promises a generous probability of sunny weather. Average cloudiness (Figure 4-3) barely budges from the 25% to 35% range from Mazatlán to the start of the Sierra Madre Oriental—a very generous climatology as eclipse travel goes. Only when the track reaches the east side of the Orientals and descends onto the Gulf Plains does the cloud cover rise, from around 30% at Monclova to near 50% at Piedras Negras and the U.S. border.

Though Mexico has a very sunny climate, approximately one-quarter to one-third of skies are cloudy enough to have an impact on viewing the eclipse. The main sources of cloudy weather are quite eclectic:

- High-level cloud carried across the region by the sub-tropical jet stream
- Cold fronts that drop southward from the U.S. Great Plains onto the Plateau
- Convective clouds that form along the eastern slopes of the Sierra Madre Occidental
- Low cloud that moves inland from the Gulf of Mexico across the Gulf Coastal Plain

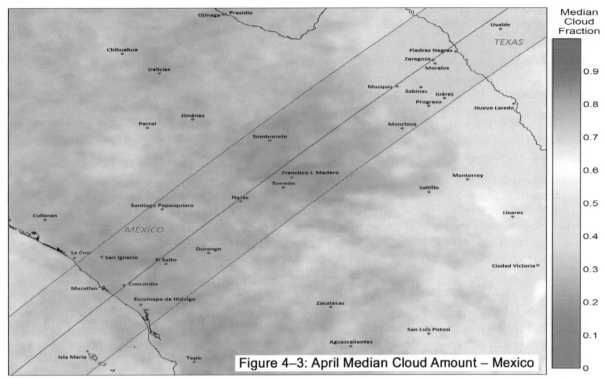

Figure 4-3: Cloud-cover map of Mexico showing the 20-year median cloud fraction at 1:30 pm local time. Cloud fraction may be treated as percentages. Data were acquired by the Aqua satellite. Data: NASA.

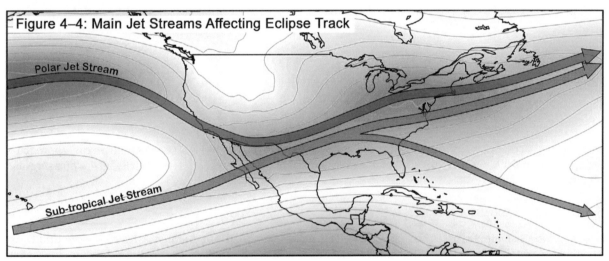

Figure 4-4: Location of the main jet streams affecting the eclipse track.

The sub-tropical jet stream (Figure 4-4) is a major annoyance for astronomers in Mexico, Arizona, New Mexico, and Texas, carrying patchy high-level cloud through the region. The jet stream is always somewhere in the neighborhood, flowing from southwest to northeast, and may impact the eclipse track anywhere from Northern Texas to Central Mexico. If the flow of wind aloft is relatively weak, the jet stream may carry no cloud at all; stronger jets will bring increasingly opaque cloud cover, typically at cirrus and high mid-cloud levels. For the most part, jet stream cloud is transparent to semi-opaque, but the energy contained in the upper winds may interact with lower atmospheric levels to intensify a cold front or promote the development of convective clouds along the slopes of the Sierra Madre Occidental.

Cold fronts that swing down into Mexico from Texas and New Mexico are a much bigger problem than the sub-tropical jet, because they can bring extensive areas of cloud with a tendency to form towering convective buildups. These fronts can penetrate deep into Mexico and certainly across the eclipse track, though they are much more intrusive on the east side of the Sierra Madre Occidental than on the Pacific side. As with all cold fronts, they come with many levels of intensity. Some bring clumpy mid- and high-level clouds. Others, more active, bring large cloud shields with embedded showers and thundershowers. Fortunately, these large systems are relatively easy to predict.

On sunny but unsettled days, convective clouds may form on the mountain ridges and on east-facing slopes, taking advantage of the absorption of sunlight by dark, forested hilltops to raise temperatures and initiate the growth of showers and thundershowers. The largest of these convective storms send cloudy debris across the Mexican Plateau to plague eclipse seekers. Finding sunshine can be challenging in a highly convective atmosphere, but the road from Durango to Torreón, which offers a route that parallels the central line for 250 km, might provide a route to escape into sunnier weather. Storms usually form later in the day, after the eclipse, and escape may be as easy as moving a little farther east.

On the narrow coastal strip around Mazatlán, convective clouds are rare and southward-sweeping cold fronts are unable to cross the 2600-m heights of the Sierra Madre Occidental. Most cloud on the Pacific side of the mountains comes from jet stream cirrus plus a small amount of morning fog that forms offshore overnight (and burns off before the eclipse). While the Mazatlán coast doesn't have the greatest sunshine along the eclipse track, it's only 3% to 5% cloudier than measured at Durango and Torreón. All-in-all, coastal Mexico probably offers the best weather prospects for the eclipse.

The least promising eclipse-watching sites in Mexico come on the Gulf Coastal Plains where low-level cloud and moisture from the Gulf of Mexico can move northwestward over flat terrain toward the eclipse track beyond Nuevo Laredo. Southeast of Monterrey, the cloud piles up against the steeper parts of the Orientals, but farther northwest, the Orientals become quite broken up, and the coastal cloud is sometimes able to worm it way west to Monclova. The impact of cold fronts dropping southward from Texas is the main reason for the 15-percent growth in cloudiness as the eclipse track leaves the Mexican Plateau and reaches the U.S. border.

Site	Average high F (C)	Average low	Record high	Recond low	Precipitation in. (mm)	Snowfall in. (cm)	Days with precipitation	Days with snow	Percent of maximum sunshine
Mexico									
Mazatlan	89 (32)	60 (16)	95 (35)	48 (9)	.06 (1.6)		0.6		67
Durango	81 (27)	47 (8)	97 (36)	21 (-6)	0.24 (6)		1		78
Torreón	91 (33)	60 (16)	106 (41)	35 (2)	0.6 (14)		1.7		62
Monclova	89 (32)	62 (17)	107 (42)	39 (4)	1.6 (40)		4.7		58
Piedras Negras	87 (31)	59 (15)	108 (42)	30 (-1)	2.0 (50)		4.5		61

Table 4-1: Climate statistics for selected sites along the eclipse track in Mexico.

Temperatures are pleasant for the most part in Mexico (Table 4-1), though the overnight lows can approach the freezing point on the Mexican Plateau. Sunshine measurements are encouraging, especially as the measurements probably underestimate the true value.

4.3 Texas to Missouri

When the Moon's shadow crosses the Rio Grande and moves into the United States, it traverses the Gulf Coastal Plain where elevations are between 200 and 300 m above sea level. Immediately afterward, the shadow meets the Balcones Escarpment and rises onto the Edwards Plateau, an increase of about 400 m in elevation. After passing San Antonio and Austin, the track descends once again onto the Coastal Plain, passing Dallas and Fort Worth on its way to the Oklahoma and Arkansas borders.

Through Oklahoma, Arkansas, and Missouri, the topography along the eclipse track is an up-and-down roller coaster with several small mountain chains interspersed with flatter plateaus. The Ouachita Mountains straddle the eclipse track across the Oklahoma-Arkansas border and farther along, the Boston Mountains underlie the north side of the shadow's path beyond Russellville, Arkansas. The track settles onto the Ozark Plateau as it moves into Missouri, and later, just touches the St Francis Mountains on its north side as it reaches the Missouri River. All along the Oklahoma to Missouri part of the track, there is lower ground to the south side of the path (the Mississippi Alluvial Plain) and higher ground to the north.

The cloud map in Figure 4-5 shows a modest increase in cloud cover from the Mexican border to the Missouri River. Most of the rise takes place in Texas where the eclipse path moves from dry-season sub-tropical climatology into mid-latitude springtime weather. April is a month that has both a summer and a winter personality, sometimes with convective thunderstorms (including severe weather) and at other times, cold-season low-pressure storm systems.

Usually, an increase in gloomy weather is expected the terrain rises and a lower amount of cloud where the terrain descends, but in Texas, where the high plains tap into the dry climatology of the Southwestern Deserts, this relationship does not hold. Instead, it is the higher elevations in the state that enjoy the better weather. The map of cloud cover (Figure 4-5) shows there are significant terrain-induced modifications to the cloud cover, but they are off to the north or south side of the central line.

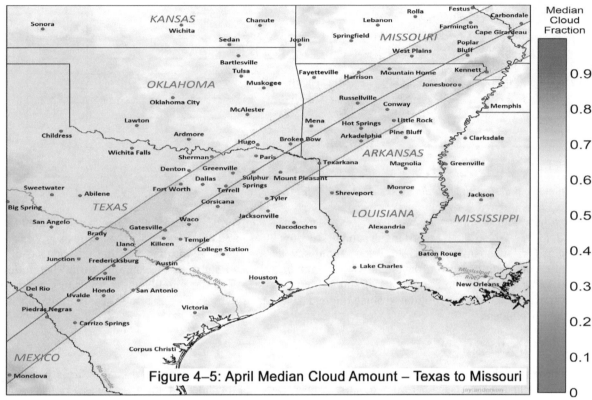

Figure 4-5: Cloud-cover map from Texas to Missouri showing the 20-year median cloud fraction at 1:30 pm local time. Data were acquired by the Aqua satellite. Data: NASA.

Across Texas, the north side of the track has a notably sunnier April climate than the south. The best of Texas weather prospects—in fact, the best prospects in the United States and Canada—lies on the Edwards Plateau between Del Rio and Brady, where median cloud amounts are as much as 15% lower than those south of the central line on the Coastal Plain. The best climatological prospects lie a little southwest of the town of Junction, 28 km inside the track, though its eclipse duration of 3m 7s is significantly shorter than the 4m 26s at the central line near Kerrville. The satellite measurements show a median April cloud fraction of 39% (0.39 on the map's scale) in the area. Junction connects to Kerrville and San Antonio by Interstate 10, which provides a convenient cross-track route to better weather between the three locations if movement is necessary on eclipse day. Don't leave it to the last minute—the 2017 eclipse taught us that even Interstates will come to a halt when the eclipse is imminent!

Another good eclipse-viewing spot is one tucked up against the Mexican border where cloud amounts are only fractionally greater than at Junction, generally between 40% and 45%. The town of Eagle Pass, opposite Piedras Negras, Mexico, may provide a convenient home base for those who wish to remain in the United States. Movement across or along track from Eagle Pass can be accomplished along State Highway 277, which leads to Del Rio to the north and Carrizo Springs to the southeast. Figure 4-5 also points to a location between Fredericksburg and Llano as a low-cloud site for those who wish to park in the middle of the umbral shadow.

Past Llano, cloud amounts climb slowly along the shadow path, rising from 47% to 56% along the eclipse central line. Mottled greenish colours in Figure 4-5 depict small pockets of higher and lower cloudiness, but these are relatively insignificant. Through Oklahoma, Arkansas, and most of Missouri, cloud cover along the track axis varies through a 5% range, between 54% and 59%. It is not until the eclipse shadow is almost in Illinois that cloudiness fraction reaches above 60%.

Beyond Little Rock, Arkansas, the south side of the shadow moves over the lowlands of the Mississippi Alluvial Plain while the north side rests on the higher terrain of the Boston Mountains and the Ozark Plateau, an elevation change of 600 m. The low-lying floodplain of the Mississippi River in northeast Arkansas and the Missouri Panhandle is a "reservoir" of atmospheric moisture that blossoms with convective clouds on unstable April days while the hills to the west remain in sunshine. It's not an everyday event, but happens often enough, especially just after larger systems have passed by to the east, that the cloud statistics are strongly affected. From Little Rock onward, it's probably best to avoid the south side of the track and head for the high ground on the Ozark Plateau unless the weather forecast promises a sunny day right across the track.

Site	Average high F (C)	Average low F (C)	Record high F (C)	Record low F (C)	Precipitation in. (mm)	Snowfall in. (cm)	Days with precipitation	Days with snow	Percent of maximum sunshine
Texas									
Austin City	80 (27)	59 (15)	99 (37)	30 (-1)	2.09 (53)		7		53
San Antonio	81 (27)	58 (15)	101 (38)	31 (-1)	2.1 (53)		6.4		54
Dallas	77 (25)	56 (13)	100 (38)	30 (-1)	3.1 (78)		6.7		61
Arkansas									
Little Rock	73 (23)	51 (11)	95 (35)	28 (-2)	5.1 (131)		9.4		71
Missouri									
St Louis	67 (20)	47 (8)	93 (34)	20 (-7)	3.7 (94)	0.4 (1)	11	0.3	56

Table 4-2: Climatological statistics for selected sites along the eclipse track from Texas to Missouri.

For the most part, average afternoon temperatures are very pleasant across the Texas to Missouri portion of the eclipse track (Table 4-2), though record highs run into the low 90s (33°C) and record lows can drop as low as the freezing point (or lower, in Missouri). In Texas, about seven days of the month report rain; in Arkansas and Missouri, rain comes on about ten days. Snowfall is largely unknown south of Missouri in April. The station statistics in Table 4-2 show the percentage of sunny hours compared to the number of hours from sunrise to sunset, but these are old data, not updated since the mid-1990s for the most part and have observational biases that limit their usefulness.

4.4 Severe Thunderstorms

Until the eclipse track passes Ohio, typical April weather can include a threat of severe thunderstorms, including tornadoes. The eclipse track passes through a dense concentration of tornado reports over Texas, Arkansas, and Illinois. Since tornadoes are fed by moisture advecting from the Gulf of Mexico, there are fewer of them on the Edwards Plateau in Texas where elevation limits the penetration of the high-humidity air.

Tornadoes are a very localized event, but the systems that spawn them also dump a large mass of mid- and high-level cloud into the atmosphere and the extent and opacity of those clouds is not always captured by the models that predict the weather. The location and initiation time of those storms is also a bit dicey, and while they can be predicted in general, their rapid formation can bring on a late and unavoidable surprise. If you can find an accomplished storm chaser to join your eclipse party, you will find them a valuable source of information and reassurance.

4.5 Illinois to Ohio

As the eclipse track reaches Illinois, it moves into the path of the mid-latitude storms: the Alberta Clipper, the Colorado Low, and their various cousins. These are names given to the more intense low-pressure systems, but there are many weaker ones that bring a day or two of cloud and then depart eastward, leaving only a few inches of snow or a small amount of rain. At this latitude, they are a regular spring event. Storms approaching from the west will first spread a thickening veil of cloud across the eclipse track and then eventually bring precipitation as they come closer and thicken. At the approach, warm southerly winds will dictate that rain is most likely in the beginning, perhaps mixed with some sort of freezing precipitation. After the storm's passage, winds turn to the north and cold air pours southward. If temperatures are low enough, the rain will change to snow—sometimes in large quantities. April still has a winter flavor, especially in the more northerly parts of the track.

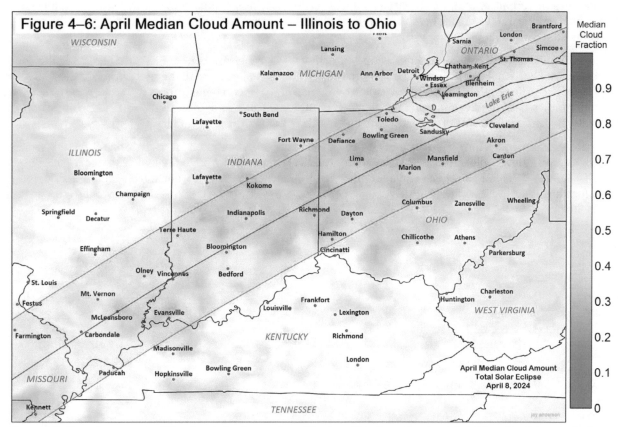

Figure 4-6: Map of average April fractional cloud cover from Illinois to Ohio for approximately 1:30 pm local time derived from 20 years of observations from the MODIS instrument aboard the Aqua satellite. Data: NASA

Along the portion of the track through Illinois, Indiana, and Ohio, there are small ups and downs in the topography, but with no substantial elevation changes that would affect the cloud climatology. More importantly, the north side of the shadow track runs over Lake Erie and later, over Lake Ontario after passing Toledo. The south limit remains well to the south and is not influenced by the lake.

In Figure 4-6, cloud amounts vary between 60% and 70% along most of the Illinois to the Ohio portion of the track. There is no dominant side for much of the path through the Midwest—first the north side and then the south has the lower or higher cloud amount. In most cases, the difference is small, less than 10%, a result that shows up as a mottled orange background in the map.

However, just as the eclipse track reaches Lake Erie, average cloudiness drops abruptly by more than 15%. Close examination of Figure 4-6 shows that this low-cloud refuges is created by the lakes, and that it is found for a short distance inland along the south shore. This implies that those low-cloud afternoons that contribute to reducing the average for the month most often come on days with a northerly component to the wind—that is, after the passage of a low-pressure disturbance. If the fresh supply of northerly air behind the low is not particularly cold, then the lake will be cloud-free, and any convective clouds will form over the land south of the lake. The water temperatures—a few degrees above freezing—cool the air and prevent the formation of convective buildups at least until the air has moved over the warmer ground.

If, however, the north winds behind a departing low carry much colder air, the flow across the lakes will generate deep convective clouds that bring "lake-effect" snow or rain showers onto the lee (south) shore. These cloud buildups can be quite deep and bring heavy rain showers or wet snow showers. As the storm departs, the north winds will subside and the convection over the lake will gradually die away. The land will not be so quick to clear however, as the heating of the ground by the Sun in the holes between the clouds is enough to maintain the convection, delaying clearing by several hours.

Air flowing off the lake doesn't immediately turn into cloud—it takes a short amount of time before heat from the ground makes its way into the atmosphere and begins to build clouds. This delay leaves a small area of clear skies along the south shore of the lakes that provides an opportunity for viewing if eclipse day is plagued by a larger low-pressure disturbance. Under such circumstances, eclipse seekers should move westward, staying close to shore, until they encounter the first of the clear air along the waterfront. This lakeshore clearing typically extends only a few kilometers inland (Figure 4-6).

The main beneficiaries of this lake-induced suppression of cloud cover are communities that lie along the south and southwest shores of Lake Erie. In particular, the city of Cleveland lies close to the spot with the lowest median cloud cover according to the satellite observations. In Canada, there is no benefit from being alongside Lake Erie, but communities between Leamington and Blenheim will profit from being downwind of Lake St. Clair, though observations the Canadian side of Lake Erie will be very close to the northern limit.

As a transitional month, April is no stranger to colder temperatures and a bit of snow. Once the track reaches Indiana, overnight lows below the freezing point are relatively common through the Midwest. Record lows reach to the 10°F (-12°C) region and the average month has 3 to 5 inches (80-120 cm) of snow (Table 4-3). A wintery day before an eclipse will make for messy travel, but snowy days are uncommon—typically only 1 to 3 in the month. Sunshine statistics show a gradual decline along the eclipse track from west to east.

Site	Average high °F (°C)	Average low F (C)	Record high F (C)	Recond low F (C)	Precipitation in. (mm)	Snowfall in. (cm)	Days with precipitation	Days with snow	Percent of maximum sunshine
Kentucky									
Paducah	69 (21)	47 (8)	90 (32)	21 (-6)	4.8 (121)	trace	11	0	
Illinois									
Cairo	70 (21)	46 (8)	94 (34)	25 (-4)	4.6 (117)		11	0	61
Indiana									
Indianapolis	63 (17)	43 (6)	90 (32)	18 (-8)	3.8 (97)	0.2 (0.5)	12	0	55
Fort Wayne	61 (16)	23 (-5)	90 (32)	7 (-14)	3.5 (89)	1 (2.5)	13	0	59
Ohio									
Cleveland	59 (15)	25 (-4)	88 (31)	10 (-12)	3.5 (89)	3.3 (8)	14	2.3	49
Toledo	60 (16)	23 (-5)	89 (32)	8 (-13)	3.2 (81)	1.3 (3)	12	1.5	52
Dayton	62 (17)	25 (-4)	90 (32)	15 (-9)	4.1 (104)	0.6 (2)	13	0.1	53
Columbus	64 (18)	43 (6)	90 (32)	14 (-10)	3.4 (86)	1.1 (3)	14	1.2	50
Ontario									
Leamington	43 (6)	28 (-2.4)	72 (22)	-2 (-19)	2.6 (67)	8.7 (22)	11	4.8	

Table 4-3: Temperature and precipitation data for the Kentucky-Ohio portion of the eclipse track.

4.6 Pennsylvania and New York

As the umbral shadow moves across Pennsylvania and then into New York, it begins to cross the northern reaches of the Appalachian Mountains and terrain-induced cloud changes become significant. The north side of the track remains over lower terrain, first in crossing Lake Ontario, and then by moving down the valley of the St. Lawrence River. The south side, in contrast, passes over the Allegheny Plateau in Pennsylvania and western New York, and then over Tug Hill Plateau and the Adirondack Mountains in northwestern New York. Over Tug Hill, elevations reach 600 m above the lake level and over the Adirondacks, the south side of the track must climb above 1200 m. Higher terrain increases the amount of April cloudiness, while lower levels and the nearby presence of lakes brings lower cloud frequencies. These changes of elevation and circumstance are mirrored in the cloud-cover map of Figure 4-7.

The cloud-cover map for Pennsylvania and New York reveals evidence of the mixed influences of topography and the water. There is a band of lower cloudiness along the south shore of Lake Erie as far east as Dunkirk, and along the south shore of Lake Ontario from Niagara Falls to Oswego and a little beyond. Rochester is particularly well located along the south shore of Lake Ontario with a median cloud amount of just over 60% for the month. As with Lake Erie, this reduction in cloudiness is caused by the suppression of convective clouds by the cooler water of the lake. Over and along the south sides of Lake Erie and Lake Ontario, there is a broad area of lower cloudiness that extends inland for 20 to 30 miles (30 to 50 km) and so a position on the south side of the lakes will give a greater likelihood of sunshine on eclipse day.

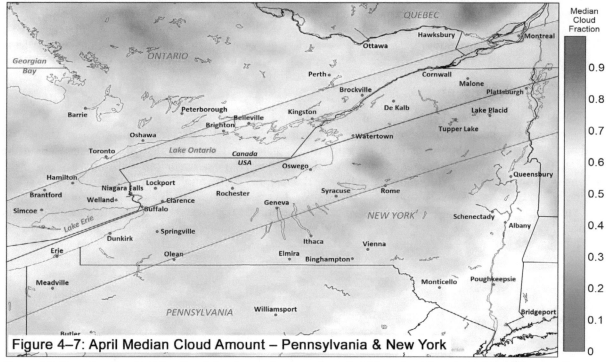

Figure 4-7: April Median Cloud Amount – Pennsylvania & New York

Figure 4-7: Map of median April fractional cloud cover for approximately 1:30 pm local time derived from 20 years of observations from the MODIS instrument aboard the Aqua satellite. Data: NASA

Just past Lake Ontario, the eclipse track begins to encounter the Appalachians, first over Tug Hill Plateau and then over the Adirondack Mountains. Cloud amounts jump upward in Figure 4-7's map, reaching a peak of 84% over Tug Hill. In this part of New York State, the lower elevations have a lower frequency of cloudy days, but the effect is small, only about 10% near Syracuse, along Oneida Lake, and about the same near Plattsburg, along Lake Champlain. On the north side of the track, there is almost no change in cloudiness, as both terrain influences and lake cooling are missing. In this part of the shadow's path, the low ground along the St Lawrence River is preferred, though even with that advantage, the cloud climatology is pessimistic.

Day-by-day examination of the satellite images shows that clearing behind a weather system proceeds regularly from west to east. Clearing along the lakefront proceeds more rapidly than farther inland. This suggests a strategy for eclipse day if circumstances permit: move westward along the south shores of Lake Ontario or Lake Erie until clear skies appear over the lake to the north. Fortunately, Interstate 90 runs from Cleveland to Buffalo along Lake Erie, barely departing more than 10 km from the water's edge. Lake Ontario is not so well served, and smaller and more winding highways will have to suffice. Highway 104 runs from Rochester eastward but leaves the waterfront and runs farther inland than seems comfortable.

Site	Average high °F (°C)	Average low F (C)	Record high F (C)	Recond low F (C)	Precipitation in. (mm)	Snowfall in. (cm)	Days with precipitation	Days with snow	Percent of maximum sunshine
Pennsylvania									
Erie	56 (13)	38 (3)	89 (32)	7 (-14)	3.3 (85)	3.2 (8)	14	2.7	
New York									
Buffalo	55 (13)	37 (3)	94 (34)	5 (-15)	3.0 (76)	2.7 (8)	13	3.1	48
Rochester	56 (13)	37 (3)	93 (34)	7 (-14)	2.7 (69)	3.9 (7)	13	3.2	51
Syracuse	57 (14)	37 (3)	93 (33)	7 (-14)	3.2 (81)	3.8 (10)	14	2.6	51
Ontario									
Hamilton	53 (12)	36 (2)	88 (31)	6 (-14)	2.9 (73)	1.1 (2.8)	14	1	45
St. Catherines	54 (12)	36 (2)	90 (32)	5 (-15)	3 (77)	2.3 (6)	14	2	42
London	54 (12)	35 (2)	87(31)	0 (-18)	3.3 (83)	3.7 (9)	14	4	39

Table 4-4: Climate statistics for selected stations along the eclipse track from Pennsylvania through New York and Ontario.

The northeastward path of the shadow brings the eclipse seeker into cooler and cooler climates. Average overnight lows through Ontario and New York flirt with the freezing point and nearly half the days of the month report precipitation of one form or another (Table 4-4). Snow days now become a possibility, though still only about 1 day in 10. The percent of maximum sunshine creeps downward with less than half the amount possible from sunrise to sunset. In such an environment, forecasts become critical in the days leading up to the eclipse.

4.7 Vermont to New Brunswick

As the shadow path crosses into Vermont, cloud amounts climb in response to the gradual northward trend of the track that takes it ever deeper into the path of storms moving across the continent. The shadow also crosses the top end of the Appalachian Mountains in this region—the roughest terrain since Mexico. The south side of the eclipse path has the bumpiest route, negotiating several sub-ranges, the most prominent of which are the Green Mountains in Vermont and the White Mountains in New Hampshire, Maine, and a part of Québec. In contrast, the north side of the track passes over the flat plains of the St. Lawrence Valley south and east of Montréal before gaining a little elevation and roughness as it reaches the Maine border and the Longfellow Mountains (a branch of the White Mountains). The Appalachians begin to peter out in northeast Maine, leaving a rugged but lower-elevation landscape for the shadow as it moves into New Brunswick toward the Gulf of St Lawrence.

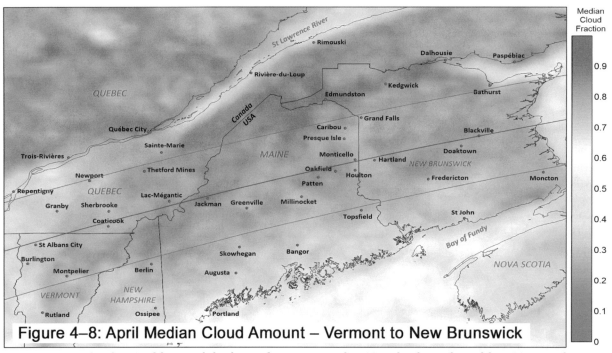

Figure 4–8: April Median Cloud Amount – Vermont to New Brunswick

Figure 4-8: Map of median April fractional cloud cover for approximately 1:30 pm local time derived from 20 years of observations from the MODIS instrument aboard the Aqua satellite. Data: NASA.

From the cloud map in Figure 4-8, it is apparent that the mountain ranges generate higher amounts of cloud over Québec, New Hampshire, and western Maine as the air rises over their heights. The drop in cloudiness over central Maine is a consequence of the downslope flow on the east side of the Longfellow Mountains, which dries the air and brings a 10% reduction in median cloudiness as the air moves to lower elevations. Individual satellite images show occasional breaks in an otherwise solid cloud cover between Millinocket and Greenville that can be attributed to the flow over the mountains. Unfortunately, the mountains have another side effect: they create occasional wave clouds that spread across much of central and eastern Maine, sometimes reaching into New Brunswick. These clouds would not dissipate during the eclipse and may even thicken up, but, because wave clouds tend to stay in place, locked in position by the mountains that form them, a lucky observer might find a sunny gap between clouds and be confident that it would remain in place, at least for enough time to capture the eclipse.

At first glance, it is difficult to be optimistic about eclipse-viewing prospects anywhere east of the Champlain Valley. Along the Maine-Québec border, cloudiness reaches 90% across the White and Longfellow Mountains and barely falls below 75% over the rest of the path through eastern Maine and over New Brunswick. Weather prospects are better at lower elevation, but not by much. Except for one place.

In Figure 4-8, there is a sharp drop in average cloud amounts as the shadow path reaches the Northumberland Strait on the east coast of New Brunswick. The largest part of this drop is over the Strait itself, as it extends only a very short distance inland. This decline in over-water cloudiness, to about 65%, is derived from a few days each April when convective clouds form over the land when the Sun warms the ground but are unable to build above the cold waters of the Strait.

Eclipse observers should give themselves the option of moving to the coast if conditions require it on April 8. The advantage gained by settling along the Northumberland shore is not large—only about 15%—but it is the lowest level of cloudiness east of Lake Ontario. The Strait's effect on the cloud cover is strongest where points of land project into the water such as at Point Escuminac or Richibucto Head (also known as Cap-Lumière).

When the *Aqua* and *Suomi* satellites makes their afternoon passage across the eclipse track, a certain number of days are affected by scattered and broken convective clouds. These cumuliform clouds contribute to the average cloudiness in the region's climatology but because they depend on the daytime heating of the ground, there is considerable likelihood that they will dissipate as the oncoming lunar shadow causes temperatures to fall. When examining the eclipse-day images for the past 20 years, several otherwise cloudy days turn out to be good candidates for shadow-induced dissipation. We estimate that the eclipse would be visible without too much effort through this area on about 40% of those April 8's, a figure that is better than the 75% average cloudiness would seem to promise.

Some support for this 40% value comes from sunshine observations collected at surface observing stations, usually at airports. The last sunshine measurement made in the United States was in 2004 (most stopped in the 1900s), but Canadian measurements are ongoing and offer some basis for comparison with the satellite. At Moncton, New Brunswick, median April sunshine amounts to 41% of the sunrise-to-sunset hours. Compare this to the 79% cloudiness from the satellite suggests that the satellite gives an overly pessimistic view of eclipse-day weather prospects. At the very least, sunshine data should reassure the eclipse traveler that things are not as bad as they seem.

Site	Average high °F (°C)	Average low F (C)	Record high F (C)	Record low F (C)	Precipitation in. (mm)	Snowfall in. (cm)	Days with precipitation	Days with snow	Percent of maximum sunshine
Vermont									
Burlington	55 (13)	35 (2)	91 (33)	2 (-17)	2.8 (72)	4.6 (12)	13	3.1	51
New Hampshire									
Berlin	51 (11)	30 (-1)	89 (32)	-9 (-23)	3.2 (82)	5.5 (14)	10	2	
Québec									
Sherbrooke	51 (10)	30 (-1)	86 (30)	-6 (-21)	3.3 (84)	2.5 (63)	15	6	40
Montréal	53 (12)	34 (1)	86 (30)	5 (-15)	3.2 (82)	5.1 (13)	12	3	44
Ontario									
Kingston	51 (10)	34 (1)	87 (31)	1 (-17)	3.4 (87)	3.2 (8)	14	2.6	40
Cornwall	54 (12)	36 (2)	87 (31)	-1 (-18)	2.8 (71)	4 (10)	11	2	41
Maine									
Millinocket	51 (11)	31 (-1)	87 (31)	-5 (-21)	3.6 (90)		8.4	3.9	
Houlton	50 (10)	28 (-2)	86 (30)	-6 (-21)	2.8 (71)	5.5 (14)	12	2.7	
New Brunswick									
Fredericton	50 (10)	31 (-0.4)	87 (31)	-4 (-20)	3.2 (82)	5.3 (14)	13	2	40
Miramichi	47 (9)	39 (4)	85 (30)	16 (-9)	3.3 (85)	10.2 (26)	15	5	39
Moncton	48 (9)	31 (-0.7)	84 (29)	0 (-18)	3.6 (92)	11.2 (29)	14	5	

Table 4-5: Climate statistics for selected stations along the eclipse track from Vermont to New Brunswick.

Once the lunar shadow moves beyond Ohio and Ontario, the promise of spring-like weather for the eclipse becomes less and less certain. From Cleveland to Montréal, climate observations show an average of 2-4 days of the month with snowfall (Table 4-4). Average monthly accumulations are relatively small, generally 1-4 inches (2.5 -10 cm) through Ohio, New York, and Ontario growing to 4-7 inches (10 – 18 cm) in Québec, Vermont, and Maine (Table 4-5). Once into New Brunswick, however, average monthly snowfall increases to more than 30 cm (12 inches), and most years there will be snow on the ground on April 8, especially in Maine and New Brunswick.

Eclipse-day movement will be difficult in Maine and New Brunswick, as both are notable for their wilderness character, and most of the roads run across the eclipse track instead of along it. The route from Bangor, Maine, to Fredericton, New Brunswick, only approximately follows the track, but will provide some room to roam. Limited mobility options will mean that eclipse-day movement decisions will have to rely on the forecasts.

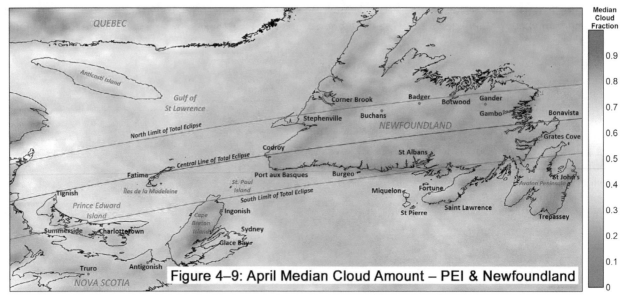

Figure 4-9: Map of April's median fractional cloud cover for approximately 1:30 pm local time derived from 20 years of observations from the MODIS instrument aboard the Aqua satellite. Data: NASA.

4.8 The Gulf of St. Lawrence and Newfoundland

After crossing Northumberland Strait, the Moon's shadow passes Prince Edward Island (PEI) and heads northeastward across the Gulf of St. Lawrence to bring Newfoundland its first eclipse since 1970. The low elevations on PEI (mostly under 40 m) and the Îles-de-la-Madeleine do not present any meteorological challenges. The south limit of the umbral track touches on the Cape Breton Highlands where elevations reach several hundred meters, but the rise in cloudiness there is mostly beyond the south limit of totality.

When the shadow reaches Newfoundland, terrain rises quickly from the shoreline as the north side of the track moves over the Annieopsquotch Mountains, east of Stephenville. The mountains are not particularly high, just under 700 m at their peak, but their influence on the cloud cover is apparent in Figure 4-9. The shadow settles onto the relatively flat terrain of Central Newfoundland, moving across a sparsely treed landscape of rolling hills until it reaches Bonavista Bay and heads out across the Atlantic.

The abrupt decline in monthly cloudiness as the eclipse track crosses Northumberland Strait is also shared by Prince Edward Island. Figure 4-9 indicates that the whole of the northwest shoreline benefits from the cloud-suppression effects of the cold water of Northumberland Strait, with cloud amounts lowering to just over 65%. The north tip of PEI (North Cape) lies just south of the eclipse midline and this location, north of Tignish, is probably the best place in Canada's Maritime Provinces from which to view the eclipse.

Beyond Prince Edward Island, the cloud cover climbs inexorably upward, from the minimum of 65% near Tignish to a discouraging 85% near Gander. There is a small upward bump as the shadow crosses the small rises in terrain in Newfoundland, and a modest decline as the shadow reaches Bonavista Bay before moving out to sea. Satellite images of Newfoundland show only one April 8 in the past 20 years where the whole island was clear, though there were several other years when partial openings or small holes in the cloud cover would have rewarded lucky observers.

Not only are clear-sky prospects limited in Newfoundland, but winter is also entrenched and only beginning to give way to the spring warming. April's morning lows are below the freezing point (Table 4-6) and precipitation is recorded on half the days of the month. Six to eight days of April get a snowfall to freshen the lingering winter snowpack and barely a third of the available daylight hours are sunny. The whole of the island is a tough place to catch a view of an eclipse. The most attractive part of eclipse watching in Newfoundland is probably Newfoundland itself.

Site	Average high °F (°C)	Average low °F (°C)	Record high °F (°C)	Record low °F (°C)	Precipitation in. (mm)	Snowfall in. (cm)	Days with precipitation	Days with snow	Percent of maximum sunshine
Prince Edward Is									
Summerside	44 (7)	30 (-1)	75 (24)	8 (-13)	3.3 (84)	8.7 (22)	15	6	39
Alberton	43 (6)	30 (-1)	73 (23)	5 (-15)	3.2 (80)	8.6 (22)	13	4	
Newfoundland									
Port aux Basques	40 (4)	29 (-2)	65 (18)	8 (-13)	5.5 (139)	6.9 (17)	16	6	
Stephenville	44 (6)	30 (-1)	75 (24)	4 (-16)	3.1 (78)	6.7 (17)	15	7	35
Bonavista	41 (5)	29 (-2)	71 (22)	8 (-14)	3.3 (83)	8.5 (22)	17	8	

Table 4-6: Climatological statistics for selected stations along the eclipse track from Prince Edward Island to Newfoundland.

4.9 Eclipse Day Planning

Except for Mexico, the 2024 Total could be a meteorological challenge. The information in this description is most useful for long-range planning but becomes less and less helpful as eclipse day approaches. By late March 2024, eclipse-day tactics should turn to the regular long- and short-range forecasts available from several agencies. On the day before the eclipse, numerical forecasts begin to lose some of their value as they are augmented by satellite and radar data and by reports from surface weather stations.

Satellites maintain a continuous watch across North America and the satellite of choice is GOES East, located over the equator and streaming images at 5-minute intervals. There are few web sites that can do proper justice to the resolution of GOES E imagery, but we can recommend the one used by storm chasers: the College of DuPage (CoD) site at weather.cod.edu. At the College, you can look at an overview of the whole of the track across Mexico, the USA, and Canada, or you can zoom in to higher-resolution views of a particular state.

Satellite photos are OK for what is happening now, but they are limited for what will happen in the next day or two. For that information, we need to use computer forecasts (usually referred to as numerical forecasts or model forecasts). For single-point forecasts, there are a wealth of private and commercial choices, but we have grown to like the SpotWeather site at spotwx.com. SpotWx will give you a model forecast for a single location and will allow you to examine several different models to make some judgement about reliability of a prediction. Commercial sites usually only show you "their" model, as they don't want to imply that there is some uncertainty in the future they foresee. In many cases, their model is the National Weather Service model with some fancy graphics attached.

A word of caution: models aren't really very good until about a week ahead of an event and improve steadily as the moment approaches. Once the different models start to look like each other, with similar cloud patterns and precipitation amounts and when successive model runs keep the same forecast, you can begin to trust them. There will always be differences, but even that will tell you where things are uncertain and help you decide whether you might want to move to a spot where they all agree about good weather.

When eclipse day arrives and the weather at your site is looking iffy, the local weather broadcast channel may be all that you need. For the most part, their forecasters concentrate on what's happening now and what will happen in the next few hours.

In the end, preparation and mobility are the most important factors.

4.10 Getting a Forecast Ahead of Eclipse Day

Weather predictions for places in North America are ubiquitous across the Internet, but there are often inconsistencies between one outlet's forecast and another's until the eclipse is only a few days away. To sort out the conflicting predictions that may arise before April 8, it helps to take a look at the output from the numerical models provided by the National Weather Service rather than a version that is post-processed to make it look more attractive. Numerical modelling of the weather is an iterative process, with forecasts becoming more and more reliable as eclipse day approaches. You must learn to adapt to these early discrepancies, especially if you are taking a long range—one or two weeks—view.

How good is the model forecast of cloud cover two weeks out? There is no way of knowing, but you can evaluate the reliability to some extent by comparing different models for the same time period. Fortunately, the United States and Canada produce several different models for the globe and North America, and if you want to go farther afield, so do the Australians, British, Europeans and several others. Don't get bogged down by looking at too many, or you will be lost in the details. Two are enough.

There are many sources for this numerical output, but here are a few that are particularly useful.

College of DuPage   Web site: https://weather.cod.edu

The College of Dupage's (CoD) weather site is a go-to address for storm chasers, as they have both long- and short-term displays of weather elements from several numerical models. Click on "Weather Analysis Tools" and select "Numerical Models." Nine tabs will give you a choice of models, and the one you will use depends on how far you are from eclipse day. The GFS is a long-range model that goes out for 15 days, but it loses reliability after about a week—you'd use it only for a general possibility of the long-term weather. There is an extensive menu is on the left, but you'll probably want to look most at the "Precipitation" tab and the "Average Cloud Cover" display. There's lots of information in the other tabs, which you can surf according to your understanding of meteorology. A slider on the bottom allows you to go forward and back in time but remember that times are in UTC and not local standard time. The date and time group is in the top right corner.

For a second opinion, you can also examine the Canadian GEM-GDPS model, another long-range numerical forecast. The European ECMWF has a reputation for being the best long-range model, but doesn't provide cloud cover forecasts on the CoD site.

Once you are within three days of the eclipse, you will find the U.S. "NAM" model and the Canadian GEM-RDPS to be more detailed (and presumably more reliable). These models have a higher resolution than the GFS and GEM-GDPS, and you should look at both of them to compare forecasts. You won't be able to tell which one is best, so use their similarities and differences to evaluate the reliability of the forecast for your chosen observing site. If they look the same, you can have a little more confidence that the model predictions are on track for eclipse day.

The NAMNST is a high-resolution version of the NAM and has a "Sim IR Satellite" display that will give you the model's version of what the infrared satellite image will look like in the future. It's a really nice display, but it only goes 60 hours into the future (the NAM goes 84 hours). If you want more than just cloud information, you can look at temperature, precipitation, and other elements in the models, keeping in mind that they will likely change as you creep up to eclipse day.

There are other models on the CoD (the HRR and the RAP), but these are rapidly updated, very short range models that are more useful for storm chasing than eclipse chasing.

Spot weather   Web site: https://spotwx.com

If you only want to look at the weather for a fixed location, or for several locations, then spotwx.com is the best option. This Canadian site shows you the model outputs from both Canadian and U.S. models in the form of a graph, and makes it easy to compare one model with another. SpotWx works anywhere in the world, as both the Canadian and U.S long-range models are global in their extent. The short-range models are largely confined to North America and nearby Mexico.

SpotWx's graphical comparisons are quite useful, as disagreements between models for a particular site is easily spotted and signal that you should be cautious about the forecast until eclipse day is a little closer. Ultimately, the models should converge on the same answer if they have any ability, but you may wish to view them for day-to-day weather well in advance of the eclipse to get an idea of their reliability. There is no easy way to tell which model is best, either overall or on a given day.

Other Web sites

There are hundreds of web sites offering access to weather models, but most of them are just replaying the output from the GFS and the NAM and there is little additional information to be had from surfing widely for a different answer. Some however, offer access to models from other countries, particularly those from Europe.

These include:

Clear Outside:	**https://clearoutside.com/forecast/50.7/-3.52**
AstroSpheric:	**https://www.astrospheric.com**
ClearDarkSky:	**https://www.cleardarksky.com/csk/**
MeteoBlue:	**https://www.meteoblue.com**
SkippySky:	**https://www.skippysky.com.au**

There is little to be gained except more uncertainty by hopping from one model to another, so don't get carried away by surfing for a different opinion.

Many commercial providers – Accuweather, Wunderground, The Weather Network—rework the information from various national meteorological agencies or occasionally, run their own models. If you can determine that these businesses are running their own models, then taking a look may help you resolve some of the uncertainty that comes with numerical predictions. Most private companies will not identify the model source of their data, and much may be owed to the U.S. National Weather Service models. One thing you are not likely to find using commercial companies is a comparison between several models. They sell certainty, not uncertainty. Nevertheless, they may use proprietary algorithms to predict secondary elements such as cloud cover and so are worth a look.

In the end, select a site that provides you with a display that appeals to you and that shows several model outputs so that you can form your own opinion about eclipse-day weather. However you obtain your model information, agreement between the differing numerical solutions gives some confidence that the forecast is reliable. If you plan to move, you can leave a little early if you are going to travel into a big area of clear skies, but if you're looking for a modest-size hole in a larger area of cloud, waiting until the last moment is probably a better idea.

Satellite Images

Models will lead you up to the day of the eclipse, but when time is being counted in hours, then your weather information will have to come from satellite images. Radar is no use—you don't need a display of where it's raining, but instead, where it isn't.

The College of DuPage site has a sophisticated site for accessing satellite images and it would be difficult to find one that offers a better product. It's accessed in the same place as the numerical models, but on a different tab. Their menu offers 26 distinct displays, but you'll want visible-light images (in red wavelengths) in the daytime and long-wave IR or some other infrared image at night. Short-wave IR works pretty good at night, as it shows low cloud well, but it isn't something you'll want to use in the day, as sunlight swamps the signal. You can zoom into a smaller region and get a look at the fine details on the CoD site. If you do your long-range planning right, the satellite images on eclipse day will allow you to find your way out of unexpected cloud movements (particularly cloud thrown up by thunderstorms) and make it into clear skies.

Photo 5–1: A team of NASA scientists prepare for the total solar eclipse of 1995 October 23 from Dundlod, India.
© 1995 by F. Espenak, www.MrEclipse.com

Section 5: Observing the Eclipse

5.1 Eye Safety and Solar Eclipses

A total solar eclipse is probably the most spectacular astronomical event that most people will experience in their lives. There is a great deal of interest in watching eclipses, and thousands of astronomers (both amateur and professional) and other eclipse enthusiasts travel around the world to observe and photograph them.

A solar eclipse offers students a unique opportunity to see a natural phenomenon that illustrates the basic principles of mathematics and science taught through elementary and secondary school. Indeed, many scientists (including astronomers) have been inspired to study science as a result of seeing a total solar eclipse. Teachers can use eclipses to show how the laws of motion and the mathematics of orbits can predict the occurrence of eclipses. The use of pinhole cameras and telescopes or binoculars to observe an eclipse leads to an understanding of the optics of these devices. The rise and fall of environmental light levels during an eclipse illustrate the principles of radiometry and photometry, while biology classes can observe the associated behavior of plants and animals. It is also an opportunity for children of school age to contribute actively to scientific research - observations of contact timings at different locations along the eclipse path are useful in refining our knowledge of the orbital motions of the Moon and Earth, and sketches and photographs of the solar corona can be used to build a three-dimensional picture of the sun's extended atmosphere during the eclipse.

Observing the partial phases of an eclipse, however, can be dangerous if the proper precautions are not taken. The solar radiation that reaches the surface of Earth ranges from ultraviolet (UV) radiation at wavelengths longer than 290 nm, to radio waves in the meter range. The tissues in the eye transmit a substantial part of the radiation between 380 and 1400 nm to the light-sensitive retina at the back of the eye. While environmental exposure to UV radiation is known to contribute to the accelerated ageing of the outer layers of the eye and the development of cataracts, the concern over improper viewing of a partial solar eclipse is the development of "eclipse blindness" or retinal burns.

Exposure of the retina to intense visible light causes damage to its light-sensitive rod and cone cells. The light triggers a series of complex chemical reactions within the cells which damages their ability to respond to a visual stimulus, and in extreme cases, can destroy them. The result is a loss of visual function which may be either temporary or permanent, depending on the severity of the damage. When a person looks repeatedly or for a long time at the Sun without proper eye protection, this photochemical retinal damage may be accompanied by a thermal injury - the high level of visible radiation causes intracellular heating that literally cooks the exposed tissue. This thermal injury or photocoagulation destroys the rods and cones, creating a small blind area. The danger to vision is significant because photic retinal injuries occur without any feeling of pain (the retina has no pain receptors), and the visual effects do not occur for at least several hours after the damage is done. (Pitts, 1993) Viewing the sun through binoculars, a telescope or other optical devices without proper protective filters can result in thermal retinal injury because of the high irradiance level in the magnified image.

The only time that the Sun can be viewed safely with the naked eye is during a total eclipse, when the Moon completely covers the disk of the Sun. *It is never safe to look at a partial or annular eclipse, or the partial phases of a total solar eclipse, without the proper equipment and techniques.* Even when 99% of the sun's surface (the photosphere) is obscured during the partial phases of a solar eclipse, the remaining crescent Sun is still intense enough to cause a retinal burn, even though illumination levels are comparable to twilight (Chou, 1981, 1996; Marsh, 1982). Failure to use proper observing methods may result in permanent eye damage and severe visual loss. This can have important adverse effects on career choices and earning potential, because it has been shown that most individuals who sustain eclipse-related eye injuries are children and young adults (Penner and McNair, 1966; Chou and Krailo, 1981; Michaelides et al, 2001).

The same techniques for observing the Sun outside of eclipses are used to view and photograph annular solar eclipses and the partly eclipsed Sun (Sherrod, 1981; Passachoff 2000; Pasachoff and Covington, 1993; Reynolds and Sweetsir, 1995). The safest and most inexpensive method is by projection. A pinhole or small opening is used to form an image of the sun on a screen placed about a meter behind the opening. Multiple openings in perfboard, a loosely woven straw hat, a colander or even between interlaced fingers can be used to cast a pattern of solar images on a screen. A similar effect is seen on the ground below a broad-leafed tree: the many "pinholes" formed by overlapping leaves creates hundreds of crescent-shaped images. Binoculars or a small telescope mounted on a tripod can also be used to project a magnified image of the Sun onto a white card. All of these methods can be used to provide a safe view of the partial phases of an eclipse to a group of observers, but care must be taken to ensure that no-one looks through the device. The main advantage of the projection methods is that nobody is looking directly at the Sun. The disadvantage of the pinhole method is that the screen must be placed at least a meter behind the opening to get a solar image that is large enough to be easily seen.

The Sun can only be viewed directly when filters specially designed to protect the eyes are used. Some of these filters have a thin layer of chromium alloy or aluminum deposited on their surfaces that attenuates both visible and near-infrared radiation. A safe solar filter should transmit less than 0.003% (density ~4.5) of visible light and no more than 3% of the near-infrared radiation between 780 and 1400 nm. (In addition to the term transmittance (in percent), the energy transmission of a filter can also be described by the term density (unitless) where density 't' is the common logarithm of the reciprocal of transmittance 't' or $d=\log10[1/t]$. A density of '0' corresponds to a transmittance of 100%; a density of '1' corresponds to a transmittance of 10%; a density of '2' corresponds to a transmittance of 1%, etc.)

One of the most widely available filters for safe solar viewing is shade number 14 welder's glass, which can be obtained from welding supply outlets. A popular inexpensive alternative is aluminized polyester that has been made specially for solar observation. (This material is commonly known as "mylar" although the registered trademark "Mylar®" belongs to Dupont, which does not manufacture this material for use as a solar filter. Note that "space blankets" and aluminized polyester film used in gardening are NOT suitable for this purpose!) Unlike the welding glass, aluminized polyester can be cut to fit any viewing device and does not break when dropped. It has been pointed out that some aluminized polyester filters may have large (up to approximately 1 mm in size) defects in their aluminum coatings that may be hazardous. A microscopic analysis of examples of such defects shows that despite their appearance, the defects arise from a hole in one of the two aluminized polyester films used in the filter. There is no large opening completely devoid of the protective aluminum coating. While this is a quality control problem, the presence of a defect in the aluminum coating does not necessarily imply that the filter is hazardous. When in doubt, an aluminized polyester solar filter that has coating defects larger than 0.2 mm in size, or more than a single defect in any 5 mm circular zone of the filter, should not be used.

An alternative to aluminized polyester that has become quite popular is "black polymer" – first developed by Thousand Oaks Optical – in which carbon particles are suspended in a resin matrix. This material is somewhat stiffer than polyester film and requires a special holding cell if it is to be used at the front of binoculars, telephoto lenses, or telescopes. Intended mainly as a visual filter, the polymer gives a yellow image of the Sun (aluminized polyester produces a blue-white image). This type of filter may show significant variations in density of the tint across its extent; some areas may appear much lighter than others. Lighter areas of the filter transmit more infrared radiation than may be desirable. The advent of high-resolution digital imaging in astronomy, especially for photographing the Sun, has increased the demand for solar filters of higher optical quality. Baader AstroSolar Safety Film, a metal-coated resin, can be used for both visual and photographic solar observations. A much thinner material, it has excellent optical quality and much less scattered light than polyester filters. Filters using optically flat glass substrates are available from several manufacturers but are quite expensive in large sizes.

Many experienced solar observers use one or two layers of black-and-white film that has been fully exposed to light and developed to maximum density. Not all black-and-white films contain silver so care must be taken to use a silver-based emulsion. The metallic silver contained in the film acts as a protective filter; however, any black-and-white negative containing images is not suitable for this purpose. More recently, solar observers have used floppy disks and compact disks (CDs and CD-ROMs) as protective filters by covering the central openings and looking through the disk media. However, the optical quality of the solar image formed by a floppy disk or CD is relatively poor compared to aluminized polyester or welder's glass. Some CDs are made with very thin aluminum coatings which are not safe – if a lighted light bulb can be seen through the CD, it should not be used! No filter should be used with an optical device (e.g. binoculars, telescope, camera) unless it has been specifically designed for that purpose and is mounted at the front end. Some sources of solar filters are listed below.

Unsafe filters include color film, black-and-white film that contains no silver (i.e. chromogenic film), film negatives with images on them, smoked glass, sunglasses (single or multiple pairs), photographic neutral density filters and polarizing filters. Most of these transmit high levels of invisible infrared radiation which can cause a thermal retinal burn. The fact that the Sun appears dim, or that you feel no discomfort when looking at the Sun through the filter, is no guarantee that the eyes are safe.

Solar filters designed to thread into eyepieces that are often provided with inexpensive telescopes are also unsafe. These glass filters often crack unexpectedly from overheating when the telescope is pointed at the Sun, and retinal damage can occur faster than the observer can move the eye from the eyepiece. Avoid unnecessary risks. Your local planetarium, science center, or amateur astronomy club can provide additional information on how to observe the eclipse safely.

There are some concerns that UVA radiation (wavelengths between 315 and 380 nm) in sunlight may also adversely affect the retina (Del Priore, 1999). While there is some experimental evidence for this, it only applies to the special case of aphakia, where the natural lens of the eye has been removed because of cataract or injury, and no UV-blocking spectacle, contact or intraocular lens has been fitted. In an intact normal human eye, UVA radiation does not reach the retina because it is absorbed by the crystalline lens. In aphakia, normal environmental exposure to solar UV radiation may indeed cause chronic retinal damage. The solar filter materials discussed in this article, however, attenuate solar UV radiation to a level well below the minimum permissible occupational exposure for UVA (ACGIH, 2022), so an aphakic observer is at no additional risk of retinal damage when looking at the sun through a proper solar filter.

In the days and weeks before a solar eclipse occurs, there are often news stories and announcements in the media, warning about the dangers of looking at the eclipse. Unfortunately, despite the good intentions behind these messages, they frequently contain misinformation and may be designed to scare people from seeing the eclipse at all. This tactic may backfire, however, particularly when the messages are intended for students. A student who heeds warnings from teachers and other authorities not to view the eclipse because of the danger to vision and learns later that other students did see it safely, may feel cheated out of the experience. Having now learned that the authority figure was wrong on one occasion, how is this student going to react when other health-related advice about drugs, AIDS, or smoking is given (Passachoff, 2001)? Misinformation may be just as bad, if not worse, than no information.

Remember that the total phase of an eclipse can and should be seen without any filters, and certainly never by projection! It is completely safe to do so. Even after observing 18 solar eclipses, the author finds the naked eye view of the totally eclipsed Sun awe-inspiring. The experience should be enjoyed by all.

Section. 5.1 was contributed by:

B. Ralph Chou, MSc, OD

Professor Emeritus, School of Optometry & Vision Science
University of Waterloo
Waterloo, Ontario, Canada N2L 3G1

References

American Conference of Governmental Industrial Hygienists Worldwide (ACGIH) (2022). TLVs® and BEIs® Based on the Documentation of the Threshold Limit Values for Chemical Substances and Physical Agents & Biological Exposure Indices. ACGIH, Cincinnati.

Chou BR (1981). Safe solar filters. Sky and Telescope 62(2):119-121.

Chou BR (1998). Solar filter safety. Sky and Telescope 95(2): 36-40.

Chou BR (1996). Eye safety during solar eclipses - myths and realities. in Z Madourian & M Stavinschi (eds.) Theoretical and Observational Problems Related to Solar Eclipses, Proceedings of a NATO Advanced Research Workshop. Kluwer Academic Publishers, Dordrecht. pp.243-247.

Chou BR and Krailo MD (1981). Eye injuries in Canada following the total solar eclipse of 26 February 1979. Can J Optom 43(1):40-45.

Del Priore LV (1999). Eye damage from a solar eclipse. in LittmanM, Willcox K, Espenak F, Totality: Eclipses of the Sun. Oxford University Press, New York, p. 140-141.

Marsh JCD (1982). Observing the sun in safety. J Brit Astron Assoc 92:6.

Michaelides M, Rajendram R, Marshall J, Keightley S (2001). Eclipse retinopathy. Eye 15:148-151.

Penner R, McNair JN (1966). Eclipse blindness - Report of an epidemic in the military population of Hawaii. Am J Ophthalmol 61:1452-1457.

Pitts DG (1993). Ocular effects of radiant energy. in DG Pitts & RN Kleinstein (eds.) Environmental Vision: Interactions of the Eye, Vision and the Environment, Butterworth-Heinemann, Toronto, p. 151.

5.2 Sources for Solar Filters

The following is a brief list of sources for filters that are specifically designed for safe solar viewing with or without a telescope. The list is not meant to be exhaustive, but is a representative sample of sources for solar filters currently available in North America and Europe. For additional sources, see American Astronomical Society Resources page: *eclipse.aas.org/resources/solar-filters*

Solar Filter Sources in the USA:

Alpine Astronomical: alpineastro.com/collections/astrosolar-viewers-and-film
American Paper Optics: www.3dglassesonline.com/products/eclipsers/
American Paperwear: ampaperwear.com/collections/solar-eclipse-glasses
Astronomics: www.astronomics.com/
Celestron: www.celestron.com/
DayStar Filters: www.daystarfilters.com/
Explore Scientific: explorescientificusa.com/collections/solar-filters
Lunt Solar Systems: luntsolarsystems.com/
Meade Instruments: www.meade.com/
OPT Telescopes: www.optcorp.com/
Orion Telescopes and Binoculars: www.telescope.com/
Rainbow Symphony: www.rainbowsymphony.com/
Seymour Solar: www.seymoursolar.com/
Spectrum Telescope: www.spectrumtelescope.com
Thousand Oaks Optical: www.thousandoaksoptical.com/

Solar Filter Sources in Canada:

Khan Scope Centre: www.khanscope.com/
KW Telescope: www.kwtelescope.com/

Solar Filter Sources in Europe:

Baader Planetarium: www.baader-planetarium.com/
First Light Optics: www.firstlightoptics.com/solar-filters.html
Rother Valley Optics: www.rothervalleyoptics.co.uk/
Solar Scope: www.solarscope.co.uk/

5.3 Eclipse Path on Google Maps

The 2024 eclipse path is also plotted on interactive Google Maps on the EclipseWise.com web site. The northern and southern path limits of an eclipse path are plotted in blue and the central lines are red. The white lines crossing the path indicate the position of maximum eclipse at 5-minute intervals. The four-way toggle arrows (upper left corner) are for navigating around the map. The zoom bar (left edge) is used to change the magnification allowing the user to zoom into the map for more detail. The two buttons (top right) turn on the map view or satellite view.

The green marker labeled GE is the point of Greatest Eclipse. The magenta marker labeled GD is the point of Greatest Duration. This is the location where the total eclipse lasts the longest along the entire path.

Clicking anywhere on a map marks a position and calculates the eclipse times at that location. Moving the cursor over a marker reveals the eclipse circumstances for that position. The marker predictions can also be viewed in a new window via the Eclipse Times Popup button. The information in the popup window can be selected, copied, and pasted into a word processor. All markers can be removed using the Clear Markers button above. Choosing the Large Map check box produces a bigger map (for users with large monitors and fast Internet connections).

The Google Map of the 2024 total solar eclipse is located at: *www.eclipsewise.com/news/2024.html*

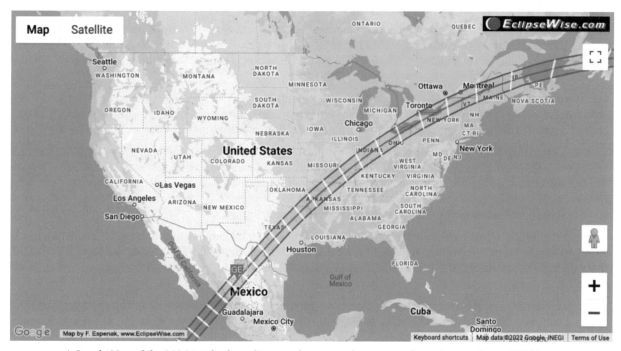

A Google Map of the 2024 total solar eclipse can be accessed at: www.eclipsewise.com/news/2024.html

Photo 5–2: Pat and Fred Espenak gaze at the Sun's corona during the total solar eclipse of 2008 August 1 from Jinta, China. © 2008 F. Espenak, www.MrEclipse.com

5.4 Sky at Totality

As the partial phases progress, the temperature drops noticeably. This can affect the focus of cameras and telescopes. The total phase of an eclipse is accompanied by the onset of a rapidly darkening sky whose appearance resembles evening twilight about half an hour after sunset. The effect presents an excellent opportunity to view planets and bright stars in the daytime sky. Aside from the sheer novelty of it, such observations are useful in gauging the apparent sky brightness and transparency during totality.

During the 2024 eclipse, the Sun will be in the constellation Pisces. Five naked-eye planets and a number of bright stars will be above the horizon within the total eclipse track. Figure 5–1 is a diagram of the sky during totality as seen from the central line at 18:15 UTC. This corresponds to central Mexico near the point of Greatest Eclipse.

The five planets lie east and west of the Sun in a string spanning 65°. The most conspicuous of the planets will be Venus (m_v= –3.9) located 15° west of the Sun. Having reached greatest western elongation in October 2023, Venus's apparent disk is 10 arc-seconds and shrinking as it approaches superior conjunction on June 4.

Jupiter is also quite bright (m_v=-2.0) and is 30° east of the Sun having passed through opposition five months earlier on 2023 November 03. Saturn and Mars lie within 1.5° of each other and 35° west of the Sun. The pair will be fainter and more difficult to see with apparent magnitudes +1.1 (Saturn) and +1.2 (Mars). Finally, little Mercury will be quite faint (m_v=+4.3) making it difficult to spot only 5.5° northeast of the Sun. The swiftest planet races to solar conjunction two months after the eclipse on June 14.

A number of bright winter stars will lying east of the Sun of may become visible during the eerie twilight of totality. They include Capella (m_v= +0.07) 65° northeast, Aldebaran (m_v= +0.99) 51° east, and Rigel (m_v= +0.28) about 63° to the southeast of the Sun. Star visibility requires a very dark and cloud free sky during the total phase.

Table 5–1 contains a geocentric ephemeris (using Bretagnon and Simon 1986) and gives the apparent positions of the naked eye planets during the eclipse. *Delta* is the distance of the planet from Earth (in astronomical units), *Apparent Magnitude* is the apparent brightness of the planet, *Apparent Diameter* of the planet is in arc-seconds, and *Elongation from Sun* is the angle between the Sun and planet (in degrees).

Table 5–1: Geocentric Solar System Ephemeris for 2024 April 08 at 18:15 UTC

Planet	RA	Dec	Delta (au)	Apparent Magnitude	Apparent Diameter	Phase	Elongation from Sun
Sun	01h11.6m	+07°35.5'	1.00151	-26.7	1916.4	-	-
Mercury	01h27.0m	+12°30.4'	0.60667	4.3	11.1	0.02	6.2E
Venus	00h18.7m	+00°27.1'	1.64687	-3.9	10.1	0.97	15.0W
Mars	22h59.8m	-07°59.8'	2.06079	1.2	4.5	0.95	36.4W
Jupiter	03h06.7m	+17°14.5'	5.85163	-2.0	33.7	1.00	29.7E
Saturn	23h05.7m	-07°50.5'	10.51192	1.1	15.8	1.00	35.0W

Figure 5–1: Sky During Totality As Seen From Central Line At 18:15 UTC

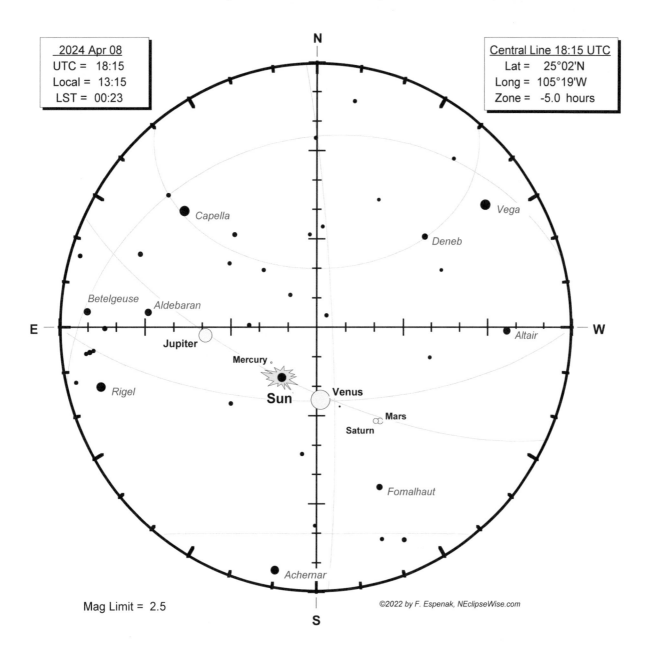

Total Solar Eclipse of 2024 Apr 08 at 18:15 UTC

Mag Limit = 2.5

©2022 by F. Espenak, NEclipseWise.com

Section 6: Eclipse Resources

6.1 Saros 139

The periodicity and recurrence of solar (and lunar) eclipses is governed by the Saros cycle, a period of approximately 6,585.3 days (= 18 years 11 days 8 hours). When two eclipses are separated by a period of one Saros, they share a very similar geometry. The eclipses occur at the same node with the Moon at nearly the same distance from Earth and at the same time of year. Thus, the Saros is useful for organizing eclipses into families or series. Each series typically lasts 12 or 13 centuries and contains 70 or more eclipses.

The total eclipse of 2024 is the 27th member of Saros series 139 (Table 6–1), as defined by van den Bergh (1955). All eclipses in an odd numbered Saros series occur at the Moon's ascending node and the Moon moves southward (i.e., gamma decreases) with each succeeding member in the family.

The series is a young one which began with a small partial eclipse at high northern hemisphere latitudes on 1501 May 17. The subsequent six eclipses were also partial, each of increasing magnitude. The first central eclipse occurred on 1627 August 11. This event was the first of a remarkable string of twelve hybrid eclipses. The eclipse of 1843 December 21 was the first total eclipse and the 20th member of the series. Subsequent eclipses were total with the duration of totality increasing with each.

Figure 6–1: Total Solar Eclipses 1970 and 1988

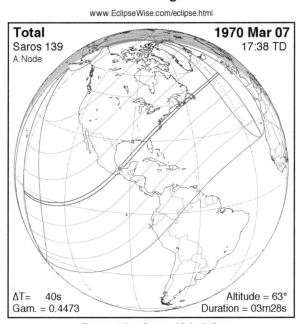
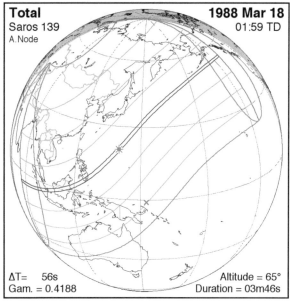

The 27th member of the series was the well-known total eclipse of 1970 March 7. The path of totality crossed southern Mexico, the southeast coast of the United States, and the Maritimes of eastern Canada. Greatest eclipse occurred over Mexico with totality lasting 3 min 28 sec. This eclipse was seen by millions of people and launched the pursuit of eclipse chasing in the modern era. It was the first total eclipse to be broadcast in color.

The path of the following event on 1988 March 18 was shifted ~120° west and crossed though Indonesia, the Philippines, and the western Pacific Ocean. The maximum duration of totality was 3 min 46 sec.

The most recent eclipse of the series took place on 2006 March 31 with the total eclipse track crossing northern Africa and central Asia. At the point of greatest eclipse the duration just broke the 4-minute mark.

One Saros period later and the path of totality returns to North America with the 2024 eclipse and a maximum duration of 4 min 28 sec.

Figure 6–2: Total Solar Eclipses of 2006, 2024, 2042 and 2186

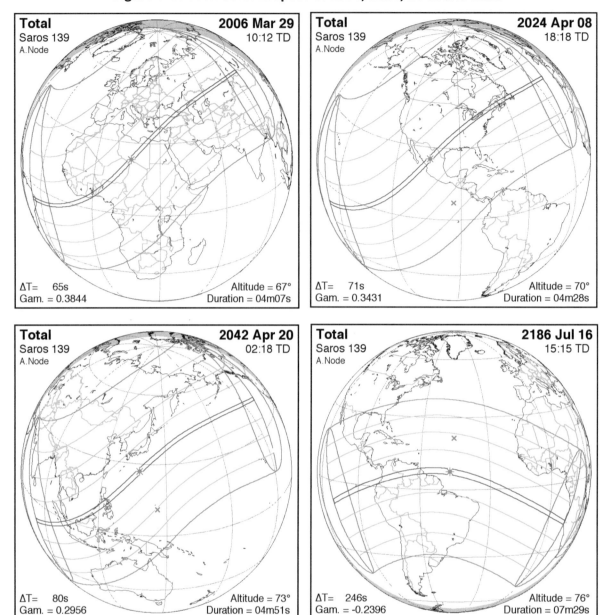

The following eclipse of Saros 139 occurs on 2042 April 20 returns to southeast Asia and the eastern Pacific. The peak duration is now approaching five minutes.

The series continues to produce total eclipses which culminates with an extraordinarily long total eclipse of 2186 July 16. The 7 min 29 sec duration falls just 3 seconds short of the theoretical maximum [Meeus, 2005]. After that date the maximum duration of each eclipse will decrease. The 2186 event has the longest duration of any eclipse over the 10,000-year interval from 4000 BCE to 6000 CE.

The last central eclipse of Saros 139 occurs on 2601 Mar 26 with a 36 second duration. The final nine eclipses are all partial events visible from the Southern Hemisphere.

A detailed list of eclipses in Saros series 139 appears in Table 6–1.

In summary, Saros 139 lasts 1262.1 years and includes 71 eclipses in the following sequence: 7 partial, 12 hybrid, 43 total, and 9 partial. A list of eclipses in Saros series 139 appears in Table 1–10. For more information and links to maps for each eclipse in the series, see:

www.eclipsewise.com/solar/SEsaros/SEsaros139.html

Table 6–1: Solar Eclipses of Saros Series 139

```
First Eclipse:    1501 May 17      Duration of Series:  1261.1 yrs.
Last Eclipse:     2763 Jul 03      Number of Eclipses:     71

Saros Summary:    Partial: 16    Annular:  0    Total: 43    Hybrid: 12
```

Date	Eclipse Type	Gamma	Mag./ Width	Center Durat.
1501 May 17	Pb	1.5003	0.0904	
1519 May 28	P	1.4189	0.2342	
1537 Jun 07	P	1.3374	0.3795	
1555 Jun 19	P	1.2542	0.5289	
1573 Jun 29	P	1.1725	0.6769	
1591 Jul 20	P	1.0911	0.8248	
1609 Jul 30	P	1.0140	0.9656	
1627 Aug 11	H	0.9401	1	00m00s
1645 Aug 21	H	0.8710	28	00m16s
1663 Sep 01	H	0.8073	38	00m29s
1681 Sep 12	H	0.7504	43	00m40s
1699 Sep 23	H	0.6999	46	00m49s
1717 Oct 04	H	0.6563	47	00m56s
1735 Oct 16	H	0.6202	48	01m02s
1753 Oct 26	H	0.5911	49	01m08s
1771 Nov 06	H	0.5676	50	01m13s
1789 Nov 17	H	0.5505	52	01m19s
1807 Nov 29	H	0.5377	55	01m26s
1825 Dec 09	H2	0.5296	60	01m34s
1843 Dec 21	T	0.5227	66	01m43s
1861 Dec 31	T	0.5187	74	01m55s
1880 Jan 11	T	0.5136	84	02m07s
1898 Jan 22	T	0.5079	96	02m21s
1916 Feb 03	T	0.4988	108	02m36s
1934 Feb 14	T	0.4868	123	02m53s
1952 Feb 25	T	0.4697	138	03m09s
1970 Mar 07	T	0.4473	153	03m28s
1988 Mar 18	T	0.4188	169	03m46s
2006 Mar 29	T	0.3843	184	04m07s
2024 Apr 08	T	0.3431	198	04m28s
2042 Apr 20	T	0.2956	210	04m51s
2060 Apr 30	T	0.2422	222	05m15s
2078 May 11	T	0.1838	232	05m40s
2096 May 22	T	0.1196	241	06m06s
2114 Jun 03	T	0.0525	248	06m32s
2132 Jun 13	Tm	-0.0186	255	06m55s
2150 Jun 25	T	-0.0911	260	07m14s
2168 Jul 05	T	-0.1660	264	07m26s
2186 Jul 16	T	-0.2396	267	07m29s
2204 Jul 27	T	-0.3129	269	07m22s

Date	Eclipse Type	Gamma	Mag./ Width	Center Durat.
2222 Aug 08	T	-0.3837	270	07m06s
2240 Aug 18	T	-0.4522	270	06m40s
2258 Aug 29	T	-0.5161	269	06m09s
2276 Sep 09	T	-0.5755	266	05m33s
2294 Sep 20	T	-0.6301	263	04m56s
2312 Oct 01	T	-0.6783	258	04m20s
2330 Oct 13	T	-0.7208	251	03m46s
2348 Oct 23	T	-0.7564	242	03m14s
2366 Nov 03	T	-0.7868	231	02m46s
2384 Nov 14	T	-0.8102	217	02m22s
2402 Nov 25	T	-0.8292	202	02m02s
2420 Dec 05	T	-0.8431	185	01m44s
2438 Dec 17	T	-0.8539	168	01m30s
2456 Dec 27	T	-0.8614	151	01m19s
2475 Jan 08	T	-0.8680	136	01m10s
2493 Jan 18	T	-0.8743	123	01m02s
2511 Jan 30	T	-0.8817	114	00m57s
2529 Feb 10	T	-0.8909	108	00m53s
2547 Feb 21	T	-0.9047	106	00m50s
2565 Mar 03	T	-0.9220	107	00m46s
2583 Mar 15	T	-0.9457	115	00m42s
2601 Mar 26	T	-0.9741	142	00m35s
2619 Apr 06	P	-1.0109	0.9780	
2637 Apr 17	P	-1.0526	0.9012	
2655 Apr 28	P	-1.1025	0.8093	
2673 May 08	P	-1.1575	0.7079	
2691 May 20	P	-1.2203	0.5921	
2709 May 31	P	-1.2869	0.4695	
2727 Jun 11	P	-1.3591	0.3371	
2745 Jun 22	P	-1.4346	0.1991	
2763 Jul 03	Pe	-1.5133	0.0561	

```
Eclipse Type:      P  - Partial        Pb - Partial Eclipse (Saros Series Begins)
                   T  - Total          Pe - Partial Eclipse (Saros Series Ends)
                   H  - Hybrid (Annular/Total)
                   H2 - Hybrid (begins Total and ends Annular)
```

Note: Mag./Width column gives either the eclipse magnitude (for Partial eclipses) or the umbral path width in kilometers (for Total and Hybrid eclipses).

6.2 EclipseWise.com Web Site

EclipseWise.com has individual web pages, maps and diagrams for every solar and lunar eclipse from 2000 BCE to 3000 CE. This amounts to 11,898 solar eclipses and 12,064 lunar eclipses. Much of the design, layout and graphics were inspired by the recent publications *Thousand Year Canon of Solar Eclipses 1501 to 2500* and the *Thousand Year Canon of Lunar Eclipses 1501 to 2500*. (See: *http://www.astropixels.com/pubs/index.html*)

The graphical user interface used by *EclipseWise.com* offers an intuitive way of accessing eclipse predictions. For example, the home page presents a concise preview of all upcoming solar and lunar eclipses over several years. Each small eclipse diagram gives a quick preview of an eclipse and links to a dedicated page for that particular eclipse.

The main or top pages of EclipseWise.com are:

Home Page (both solar and lunar eclipses): *www.eclipsewise.com/eclipse.html*
Solar Eclipses Page: *www.eclipsewise.com/solar/solar.html*
Lunar Eclipses Page: *www.eclipsewise.com/lunar/lunar.html*

6.3 Web Sites on the 2024 Eclipse

Web Site: EclipseWise.com/news/2024.html

EclipseWise.com has a series of pages and resources devoted to the 2024 eclipse. The main page (shown above) provides links to detailed eclipse path maps, tables of local eclipse circumstances for hundreds of cities, weather prospects along the eclipse path, and more. The link to an interactive Google Map with the eclipse path plotted on it allows the user to zoom into an part of the path. Click on any point on the map to display the eclipse circumstances and duration of totality at that location.

Other features include information on eye safety, eclipse photography, the sky during totality and additional data tables about the eclipse path. This web site will continue to add features as the eclipse approaches.

Web Site: GreatAmericanEclipse.com

GreatAmericanEclipse.com is published by Michael Zeiler and Polly White to educate the public on how to witness nature's greatest spectacle, a total eclipse of the Sun. Contributions in the form of guest blog posts, recommended viewing sites for a state, photographs of past solar eclipses, scans of historic drawings and maps, and similar items are welcome. Email GreatAmericanEclipse@gmail.com with text and images and your contributions will be considered for insertion if they are relevant, of high quality, and authored by you or in the public domain.

Web Site: eclipse2024.org

eclipse2024.org has been established to provide information to news media, elected officials, school administrators and teachers, and the general public on how to view the total solar eclipse of 2024. Maintained by Dan McGlaun (a veteran of 12 total solar eclipses), this site will continue to grow additional information and late breaking news of events surrounding the eclipse.

6.4 Additional Web Sites On Solar Eclipses

Below is a brief list of some notable web sites on solar eclipses.

Being in the Shadow (Dr. Kate Russo): *www.beingintheshadow.com/*
Eclipse-Chasers.com (Bill Kramer): *www.eclipse-chasers.com/Map.html*
Eclipse-Maps.com (Michael Zeiler): *www.eclipse-maps.com/Eclipse-Maps/Welcome.html*

EclipseGuy (David Makepeace): eclipseguy.com/
Eclipsophile (Jay Anderson's Eclipse Meteorology): *eclipsophile.com*
EclipseWise.com (Fred Espenak): *www.eclipsewise.com/eclipse.html*
Eclipse Photography (Miloslav Druckmüller): *www.zam.fme.vutbr.cz/~druck/eclipse/Index.htm*
Hermit Eclipse: *moonblink.info/Eclipse*
IAU Working Group on Eclipses: sites.*williams.edu/iau-eclipses/*
Interactive Eclipse Maps (Xavier Jubier): *xjubier.free.fr/en/site_pages/SolarEclipsesGoogleMaps.html*
International Occultation Timing Association (IOTA): *www.lunar-occultations.com/iota/iotandx.htm*
MrEclipse.com (Fred Espenak): *www.mreclipse.com/MrEclipse.html*
NASA Eclipse Web Site (Fred Espenak): *eclipse.gsfc.nasa.gov/eclipse.html*
Shadow & Substance (Larry Koehn): *shadowandsubstance.com/*
Solar Eclipse Mailing List (SEML): *groups.yahoo.com/neo/groups/SEML/info*
Solar Eclipses (Date and Time): *www.timeanddate.com/eclipse/total-solar-eclipse.html*
The Clock Tower (Sheridan Williams): *www.clock-tower.com/*
UMBRAPHILLIA (Dr. Glenn Schneider):
      nicmosis.as.arizona.edu:8000/ECLIPSE_WEB/UMBRAPHILE/UMBRAPHILE.html
USNO Eclipse Portal (USNO): *astro.ukho.gov.uk/eclbin/query_usno.cgi*
Waiting For The Shadow (Joe Cali*): joe-cali.com/eclipses/*
Williams College Solar Eclipse Expeditions (Jay M. Pasachoff): *web.williams.edu/Astronomy/eclipse/*
      and *totalsolareclipse.org*
Eclipses: Rice Space Institute (Patricia Reiff): *space.rice.edu/eclipse/*
Solar Eclipse (Exploratorium, San Francisco, California): www.exploratorium.edu/eclipse
WhenIsTheNextEclipse.com (Jamie Carter): *whenisthenexteclipse.com*

6.5 IAU Working Group on Eclipses

As of the 2015 reorganization of Divisions and Commissions of the International Astronomical Union, functions of both the original Working Group on Solar Eclipses of the International Astronomical Union of the Solar Division and the Program Group on Public Education at the Times of Eclipses and Transits have been combined in an Inter-Divisional Working Group.

Professional scientists are asked to send descriptions of their eclipse plans to the Working Group on Eclipses of the International Astronomical Union (IAU), so they can keep a list of observations planned. Send such descriptions, even in preliminary form, to:

International Astronomical Union/
Working Group on Eclipses
Prof. Jay M. Pasachoff, Chair
Williams College–Hopkins Observatory
Williamstown, MA 01267, USA
Fax: (413) 597-3200
E-mail: eclipse@williams.edu
Web Site: *www.eclipses.info*

The members of the Working Group on Eclipses of the Solar Division of the IAU are: Jay M. Pasachoff (USA), Chair, Jay Anderson (Canada), Fred Espenak (USA), Beatriz García (Argentina), Michael Gill (UK), Hiroki Kurokawa (Japan), Xavier Jubier (France), Iraida S. Kim (Russia), William Kramer (USA), Andreas Müller (Germany), Zhongquan Qu (China), Patricio Rojo (Chile), Glenn Schneider (USA), Jagdev Singh (India), Michael Wheatland (Australia), and Michael Zeiler (USA). Working Group Associates include B. Ralph Chou (Canada) and Michael Kentrianakis (USA).

To ensure that astronomers and public health authorities have access to information on safe viewing practices, the IAU's Commission on Education and Development, set up a Program Group on Public Education at the Times of Eclipses and Transits, now combined with the Working Group on Solar Eclipses. Under Prof. Pasachoff, the Commission assembled information on safe methods of observing solar eclipses, eclipse-related eye injuries, and samples of educational materials on solar eclipses. (see *www.eclipses.info*).

For more information, contact Prof. Pasachoff., *eclipse@williams.edu*

6.6 AAS Eclipse Planning Workshops

The Solar Eclipse Task Force of the American Astronomical Society is organizing a series of workshops on the 2023 1nd 2024 solar eclipses. The main goal of these workshops is to pursue the execution of the tasks needed to best prepare the public and the nation for this event. The activities identified by the tasks are driven by the collective and contagious enthusiasm of amateurs and professionals alike.

Web Site: *https://eclipse.aas.org/workshops*

6.7 Solar Eclipse Mailing List

The Solar Eclipse Mailing List (SEML) is an electronic news group dedicated to solar eclipses. Published by British eclipse chaser Michael Gill (eclipsechaser@yahoo.com), it serves as a forum for discussing anything and everything about eclipses and facilitates interaction between both the professional and amateur communities.

The SEML is hosted at *https://groups.io/g/SEML*

6.8 Total Solar Eclipse of 2045 August 12

The next total solar eclipse to pass across the USA from coast to coast will not occur until 2045 August 12. It will be unusually long with a maximum duration of totality of 6 min 6 sec. The path of totality spans fourteen states: California, Nevada, Utah, Colorado, Kansas, Oklahoma, Texas, Missouri, Arkansas, Mississippi, Louisiana, Alabama, Georgia and Florida. The path continues on through Haiti, Dominican Republic, Venezuela, Guyana, French Guiana, Suriname and Brazil. A partial list of some of the larger US cities in the path of totality include Reno, Salt Lake City, Colorado Springs, Oklahoma City, Tulsa, Tampa, Orlando, Fort Lauderdale and Miami.

For more information on the 2045 total solar eclipse, visit *EclipseWise.com* at:

eclipsewise.com/solar/SEprime/2001-2100/SE2045Aug12Tprime.html

Figure 6–3: Total Solar Eclipses of 2045 August 12

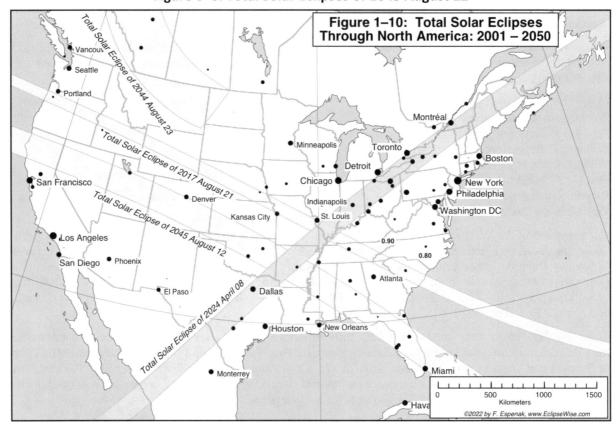

Every total solar eclipse through North America includes the eclipse of 2045 August 12.

6.9 Total Solar Eclipses Through the USA During the 21st Century

The 2024 eclipse is the second of 9 total solar eclipses visible from parts of the contiguous United States during the 21st century. The eclipses occur during the years 2017, 2024, 2044, 2045, 2052, 2071, 2078, 2079, and 2099. The figure below contains a global map of each of these eclipses.

For more information on each of these eclipses, visit *EclipseWise.com* at:

eclipsewise.com/solar/SEnews/USA21.html

Figure 6–4: Total Solar Eclipses Through the USA During the 21st Century

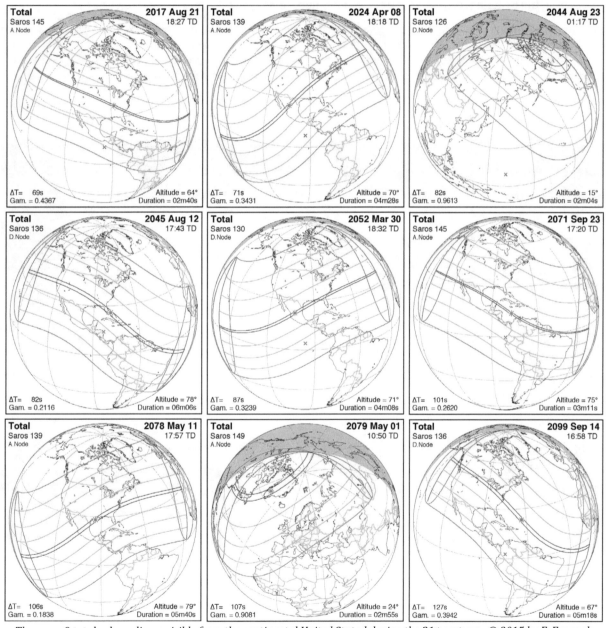

*There are 9 total solar eclipses visible from the continental United Stated during the 21st century. © 2015 by F. Espenak, courtesy of **Thousand Year Canon of Solar Eclipses: 1501 – 2500**, http://astropixels.com/pubs/TYCSE.html*

6.10 Algorithms, Ephemerides, and Parameters

The algorithms and software for the eclipse predictions were developed primarily from the *Explanatory Supplement* (Her Majesty's Nautical Almanac Office, 1974) with additional algorithms from Meeus et al. (1966), and Meeus (1989). The solar and lunar ephemerides were generated from the JPL DE430. All eclipse calculations were made using a value for the Moon's radius of k=0.2722810 for umbral contacts, and k=0.2725076 (adopted IAU value) for penumbral contacts. Center of mass coordinates for the Moon have been used without correction to the lunar limb profile except where noted. The difference between Terrestrial Time (TT) and Coordinated Universal Time (UTC) used in these predictions is 69.184 seconds (= 32.184 seconds plus 37 leap seconds). The international convention of presenting date and time in descending order has been used throughout the bulletin (i.e., year, month, day, hour, minute, second).

The primary source for geographic coordinates used in the local circumstances tables is *The New International Atlas* (Rand McNally 1991). The names and spellings of countries, cities, and other geopolitical regions are not authoritative, nor do they imply any official recognition in status. Corrections to names and geographic coordinates are actively solicited in order to update the database for future eclipse bulletins.

Photo 6–1: A dazzling diamond ring effect preceeds the start of totality during the total solar eclipse of 2019 July 02 from Vicuña, Chile. © 2019 F. Espenak, www.MrEclipse.com

Bibliography

References

Astronomical Almanac for 1986, Washington: US Government Printing Office, (1985).

Bretagnon, P., and J. L. Simon, *Planetary Programs and Tables from −4000 to +2800*, Willmann-Bell, Richmond, Virginia, 151 pp (1986).

Espenak, F., *Road Atlas for the Total Solar Eclipse of 2024 − Color Edition*, Astropixels Publishing, Portal, Arizona, 40 pp (2017).

Espenak, F., *21st Century Canon of Solar Eclipses − Color Edition*, Astropixels Publishing, Portal, Arizona, 186 pp (2016).

Espenak, F., *Thousand Year Canon of Solar Eclipses: 1501 to 2500*, Astropixels Publishing, Portal, Arizona, 294 pp (2014).

Espenak, F., and J. Meeus, *Five Millennium Canon of Solar Eclipses: −1999 to +3000 (2000 BCE to 3000 CE)*, NASA Tech. Pub. 2006-214141, NASA/GSFC, Greenbelt, Maryland, 648 pp (2006).

Herald, D., "Correcting predictions of solar eclipse contact times for the effects of lunar limb irregularities". J. Brit. Ast. Assoc., 93, 241–246 (1983).

Meeus, J., C. C. Grosjean, and W. Vanderleen, *Canon of Solar Eclipses*, Pergamon Press, N.Y., 779 pp. (1966)

Her Majesty's Nautical Almanac Office, *Explanatory Supplement to the Astronomical Ephemeris and the American Ephemeris and Nautical Almanac*, prepared jointly by the Nautical Almanac Offices of the United Kingdom and the United States of America, London, 534 pp (1974).

Pasachoff, J. M., "Public Education in Developing Countries on the Occasions of Eclipses." In: A.H. Batten, Ed., Astronomy for Developing Countries, IAU special session at 24th General Assembly, 101–106 (2001).

Pasachoff, J. M., and M. Covington, *Cambridge Guide to Eclipse Photography*, Cambridge University Press, Cambridge and New York, 143 pp (1993).

Rand McNally, *The New International Atlas*, Chicago/New York/San Francisco, 560 pp (1991).

Reynolds, M. D., and R. A. Sweetsir, *Observe Eclipses*, Astronomical League, Washington, DC, 92 pp (1995).

van den Bergh, *Periodicity and Variation of Solar (and Lunar) Eclipses*, Tjeenk Willink, and Haarlem, Netherlands (1955).

Further Reading on Eclipses

Brewer, B., *Eclipse*, Earth View, Seattle, Washington, 112 pp (2017).

Brunier, S., *Glorious Eclipses*, Cambridge University Press, New York, 192 pp (2001).

Covington, M., *Astrophotography for the Amateur*, Cambridge University Press, Cambridge, 346 pp.

Espenak, F., and J. Meeus., *Five Millennium Catalog of Solar Eclipses: −1999 to +3000 (2000 BCE to 3000 CE)*, NASA Tech. Pub. 2008-214170, NASA GSFC, Greenbelt, Maryland, 270 pp (2008).

Espenak, F., *Thousand Year Canon of Lunar Eclipses: 1501 to 2500*, Astropixels Pub., Portal, AZ, 298 pp (2014).

Espenak, F., *21st Century Canon of Solar Eclipses*, Astropixels Pub., Portal, AZ, 198 pp (2016).

Golub, L., and J. M. Pasachoff, *The Solar Corona*, Cambridge University Press, Cambridge, MA, 390 pp (2010).

Golub, L., and J. M. Pasachoff, *Nearest Star: The Surprising Science of Our Sun*, 2nd ed.Cambridge University Press, Cambridge, MA, 297 pp (2014).

Golub, L, and Pasachoff, J. M., *The Sun*, Reaktion Books (London) for the Science Museum (London), U. Chicago Press (2017).

Guillermier, P., and S. Koutchmy, *Total Eclipses, Science, Observations, Myths and Legends*, Springer, New York, 247 pp (1999).

Harrington, P. S., *Eclipse!*, John Wiley and Sons, New York, 280 pp (1997).

Maunder, M., and P. Moore, *The Sun in Eclipse*, , Springer, New York, 211 pp (1998).

Mitchell, S. A., *Eclipses of the Sun*, Columbia University Press, New York, 425 pp (1923).

Meeus, J., *Elements of Solar Eclipses: 1951–2200*, Willmann-Bell, Inc., Richmond, Virginia, 112 pp. (1989)

Meeus, J., *Astronomical Algorithms*, Willmann-Bell, Inc., Richmond, Virginia, 477 pp (1998).

Mobberley, M., *Total Solar Eclipses and How to Observe Them*, Springer, New York, 202 pp (2007).

Mucke, H., and Meeus, J., *Canon of Solar Eclipses: −2003 to +2526*, Astronomisches Büro, Vienna, Austria, 908 pp (1983).

Ottewell, G., *The Understanding of Eclipses*, Astronomical Workshop, Greenville, South Carolina, 96 pp (1991).

Olson, Roberta J. M. and Pasachoff, Jay M. *Cosmos: The Art and Science of the Universe*, Reaktion Books (London), U. Chicago Press (2019).

Pasachoff, J.M., *Field Guide to the Stars and Planets*, 5th edition, Houghton Mifflin Harcourt/HarperCollins, Boston, Massachusetts, 578 pp (2023, in preparation).

Pasachoff, J. M., *The Complete Idiot's Guide to the Sun*, Alpha Books, Indianapolis, Indiana, 360 pp (2004).

Pasachoff, J. M., "Observing solar eclipses in the developing world. In: Astronomy in the Developing World, Proc. IAU Special Session 5, J.B. Hearnshaw and P. Martinez, eds., Cambridge University Press, New York, 265–268 (2007).

Pasachoff, J. M., Fraknoi, A., "Resource Letter OSE-1: Observing solar eclipses," Am. J. Phys. 85, 485 (2017).

Pasachoff, J. M., "Heliophysics at total solar eclipses," Nat. Astron. 1, 0190 (2017).

Pasachoff, J..M., "Eclipse science today," a Quick Study for Physics Today, 72 (8), August, pp. 66-67 (2019). Correction: Physics Today 72 (10), 13 (2019).

Russo, K., *Total Addiction: The Life of an Eclipse Chaser*, Springer, New York, 193 pp (2012).

Steel, D., *Eclipse, The Celestial Phenomenon That Changed the Course of History*, Joseph Henry Press, Washington, DC, 492 pp (2001).

Todd, M. L., *Total Eclipses of the Sun*, Little, Brown, and Co., Boston, Massachusetts, 273 pp (1900).

von Oppolzer, T. R., *Canon of Eclipses*, Dover Publications, New York, 376 pp (1962).

Zirker, J. B., *Total Eclipses of the Sun*, Princeton University Press, Princeton, New Jersey, 228 pp (1995).

Further Reading on Meteorology

Griffiths, J. F., Ed., World Survey of Climatology, Vol. 10, Climates of Africa, Elsevier Pub., N.Y., 604 pp (1972).

National Climatic Data Center, International Station Meteorological Climate Summary; Vol. 4.0 (CD-ROM), NCDC, Asheville, North Carolina (1996).

Schwerdtfeger, W., Ed., *World Survey of Climatology*, Vol. 12, Climates of Central and South America, Elsevier Publishing Company, New York, 532 pp (1976).

Wallen, C. C., Ed.,: *World Survey of Climatology*, Vol. 6, Climates of Central and Southern Europe, Elsevier Publishing Company, New York, 258 pp (1977).

Warren, S. G., C. J. Hahn, J. London, R. M. Chervin, and R. L. Jenne,, Global *Distribution of Total Cloud Cover and Cloud Type Amounts Over Land*. NCAR Tech. Note NCAR/TN-273+STR and DOE Tech. Rept. No. DOE/ER/60085-H1, U.S. Department of Energy, Carbon Dioxide Research Division, Washington, DC, (NTIS number DE87-006903), 228 pp (1986).

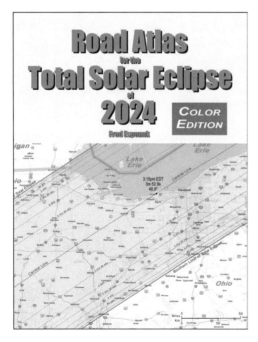

The ***Road Atlas for the Total Solar Eclipse of 2024*** contains a comprehensive series of 26 maps of the **2024 April 8** path of totality across Mexico, the USA and Canada. The large scale (1 inch ≈ 22 miles) shows both major and minor roads, towns and cities, rivers, lakes, parks, national forests, wilderness areas and mountain ranges.

Although a partial eclipse will be seen from all of North America, the total phase in which the Moon completely covers the Sun (known as totality) will only be seen from within the 120-mile-wide path of the Moon's umbral shadow as it sweeps across Mexico, the United States (Texas, Oklahoma, Arkansas, Missouri, Tennessee, Kentucky, Illinois, Indiana, Ohio, Michigan, Pennsylvania, New York, Vermont, New Hampshire, and Maine), and Canada (Ontario, Quebec, New Brunswick, Prince Edward Island, Nova Scotia and Newfoundland).

Armed with this atlas and the latest weather forecasts, the road warrior is ready to chase totality no matter where it takes you along the entire path.

For more information visit
http://astropixels.com/pubs/index.html

AstroPixels Publishing

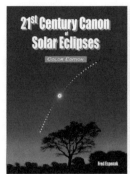 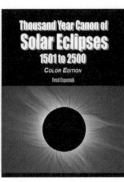 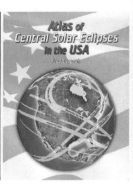 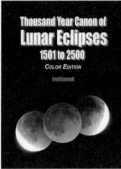 

21st Century Canon of Solar Eclipses

The complete guide with maps and data for all 224 solar eclipses occurring during the 100-year period from 2001 through 2100. A is comprehensive catalog lists the essential characteristics of each eclipse. A series of maps depict the geographic regions of visibility of each eclipse with 12 maps per page. There are full-page maps of every eclipse from 2017 through 2066. An appendix plots the track of every central eclipse (total, annular and hybrid) on large-scale maps with countries borders and major cities.

Thousand Year Canon of Solar Eclipses: 1501 – 2500

Contains maps and data for each of the 2,389 solar eclipses occurring over the ten century period centered on the present era. Some of the topics covered include eclipse classification, the visual appearance of each eclipse type, and eclipse predictions. The frequency each eclipse type, extremes in eclipse magnitude, greatest central duration are described. A comprehensive catalog lists the essential characteristics of each eclipse. An atlas of maps show the geographic regions of visibility of each eclipse. The 2,389 maps are arranged twelve to a page at an image scale permitting the assessment of eclipse visibility from any location on Earth.

Atlas of Central Solar Eclipses in the USA

When was the last total eclipse through the USA and when is the next? How often do they happen? What total eclipse tracks passed across the USA during the 17th, 18th, and 19th centuries, etc., and what states did they include? And how often is a total solar eclipse visible from each of the 50 states? The Atlas of Central Solar Eclipses in the USA answers all of these questions and more with hundreds of maps and tables.

Thousand Year Canon of Lunar Eclipses: 1501 – 2500

Contains diagrams, maps and data for each of the 2,424 lunar eclipses occurring over the ten century period centered on the present era. Some of the topics covered include eclipse classification, the visual appearance of each eclipse type, and eclipse predictions. The frequency each eclipse type, extremes in eclipse magnitude and duration are discussed. A comprehensive catalog lists the essential characteristics of each eclipse. A comprehensive catalog lists the essential characteristics of each eclipse. An atlas shows path of the Moon through Earth's shadows and maps of geographic visibility of each eclipse. The 2,424 figures are arranged twelve to a page at an image scale permitting the assessment of eclipse visibility from any location on Earth.

21st Century Canon of Lunar Eclipses

The complete guide to every lunar eclipse occurring from 2001 tom 2100 (228 eclipses in all). It includes information and maps for all total, partial, and penumbral eclipses. The predictions use a new model for Earth's shadows. The 2,389 maps and diagrams are arranged twelve to a page to show the visibility of each eclipse.

All books are available it two editions: 1) Black and White, and 2) Color. For more information including sample pages of each, visit:

http://astropixels.com/pubs/index.html

Made in United States
Troutdale, OR
02/19/2024

17823908R00060